THE DUFFER'S GUIDE
TO THE MEDIEVAL CHURCH

Josephine Laffin graduated from the University of
Adelaide in 1990 with an MA in history. She is
currently Church History lecturer for the Flinders
University of South Australia and the Adelaide
College of Divinity.

The Duffer's Guide to the Medieval Church

THE TUTORIAL NOTES OF MICHAEL ALEXANDER

Josephine Laffin

Marshall Pickering

An Imprint of HarperCollins*Publishers*

Marshall Pickering is an Imprint of
HarperCollins*Religious*
Part of HarperCollins*Publishers*
77–85 Fulham Palace Road, London W6 8JB

First published in Great Britain
in 1995 by Marshall Pickering

1   3   5   7   9   10   8   6   4   2

Copyright © 1995 Josephine Laffin

Josephine Laffin asserts the moral right to be
identified as the author of this work

A catalogue record for this book is
available from the British Library

ISBN 0 551 03011 9

Printed and bound in Great Britain by
HarperCollinsManufacturing Glasgow

Contents

WEEK·ONE

Why study medieval church history?

Ready to begin another term of church history. The new tutorial group is almost the same as last year's one for early church history. Derek is still our tutor, Christobel is still intending to be the first female Anglican archbishop, Kirsty is looking younger and prettier than ever, Maureen older but more self-assured, Ruth serene, Wade slightly bored, and Frank full of the joy of the Lord. The only person missing is Neville (he's gone to Africa to work for Community Aid Abroad). We have, however, gained two new students. Melinda looks awfully sophisticated and elegant, in a rather intimidating sort of way, and has a surname with a hyphen in it. Jason, on the other hand, wears torn, faded jeans, a Greenpeace T-shirt, long hair in a ponytail, and an earring in one ear!

Derek welcomed us to the course and rather tentatively asked, 'Why have you decided to study medieval church history?'

Kirsty said that the Middle Ages sounded sort of romantic. Wasn't it the time of King Arthur, Robin Hood, the crusades, and the Knights of the Round Table rescuing damsels in distress?

Christobel swiftly pointed out that legends which stereotype women as brainless, fragile sex objects are totally unacceptable in today's society.

This prompted Maureen to reveal that since her divorce she can't stand reading romantic trash.

Christobel sympathetically asked how she was coping.

'Well, I don't mind admitting that it's been a hell of a year so far,' she remarked frankly. 'When you're over fifty everything begins to degenerate: your figure, your eyesight, your bones. My arthritis has been shocking lately, and I've had to shift house and find a part-time job, but studying early church history did me so much good last year (you know, by taking my mind off OTHER THINGS) that I'm determined to do the medieval course, even if it kills me!'

'I . . . er . . . hope that it won't be that bad,' said Derek uneasily. 'Er . . . Melinda, why have you decided to study medieval church history?'

'Actually, I wanted to do the course on the Reformation,' Melinda acknowledged with a smile, 'but it was not offered this term. However, studying the decline and decay of the Church in the Middle Ages should prepare me for the Reformation next year.'

'Couldn't you do anything else?' asked Maureen.

'Unfortunately, the only alternative that I could fit into my schedule was quite unacceptable: the theology subject God, Science and Creation.'

'Oh, I did that a couple of years ago,' gushed Christobel. 'It was absolutely fascinating!'

'But, from what I have heard, it is taught from a very . . . you know . . . liberal perspective,' said Melinda distastefully. 'Quite unbiblical.'

'Liberal theology can be very challenging,' observed Wade.

'And I absolutely love to be challenged!' cried Christobel, glaring at Melinda. 'It was frightfully challenging considering the role of women in the early church last year, and I am now looking forward to reading about all those wonderful medieval female mystics . . .'

'Well, I don't know anything about mystics,' put in Frank, 'but there were a couple of other subjects that I could have done this term, so I prayed for guidance and really felt that God wanted me to do this one.'

Jason stared at him incredulously.

'I'm an atheist and I never wanted to do any history course, let alone a Christian one. I'm only here now because the university computer stuffed up my enrolment details, and I've learnt from bitter experience that it's easier to go along with the computer than try to get anything changed.'

'What degree are you studying for?' asked Derek worriedly.

'Bachelor of Arts,' replied Jason in a nonchalant tone. 'But I suppose it could be worse. I've already done some economics and environmental studies subjects which are relevant to today, so I can afford to waste a term on history.'

'You might find that a study of medieval political, social and economic systems will help you understand the modern world,' responded Wade. 'I suspect that the legacies of the Middle Ages are far greater than we realize!'

'Yes,' agreed Ruth, 'particularly with regard to the Church.'

'Some churches more than others,' muttered Frank.

'I . . . er . . . wanted to start this course by encouraging you to think about why we study m-medieval history, because there are different approaches to the so-called "Middle Ages",' stuttered Derek. 'During the fifteenth-century Renaissance, the sixteenth-century Reformation and the eighteenth-century Enlightenment scholars tended to . . . er . . . regard the time between the classical Roman Empire and the Renaissance as a "middle age" of decline and decay. In the nineteenth century a romantic movement arose which appreciated medieval literature, courtly love poetry, the concept of chivalry, and so on. In this century there has been considerable research into medieval history which has been quite . . . er . . . quite . . .'

'Challenging,' supplied Christobel helpfully.

'Er . . . yes,' agreed Derek weakly, 'and I hope that you will all come to realize that there was a lot more to the Middle Ages than decline and decay.'

It was time to decide who would lead the various tutorials listed in the course outline. Kirsty asked if she could take the one on the crusades in week 7, and Wade said that he would like to look at St Francis of Assisi in week 11. Christobel grabbed medieval women in week 12, and Maureen asked if the tutorial on the Franks had anything to do with France. When Derek acknowledged that it did, she said that she'd take it. Her best friend Enid is trying to get her to go on a bus tour of France later in the year, and, although she can't really afford it, her children are insisting that she go because after all that she's been through she deserves a break. Furthermore, her daughter Gail is expecting her first baby (and Maureen's first grandchild) in three months' time, so she would like to get her tutorial well out of the way before then. That settled, Frank rather surprisingly opted for the papacy in week 6, and Ruth volunteered to take monasticism in week 5.

Derek asked Melinda which of the remaining topics she would like to do. She didn't look as though she found any of them very appealing, but she eventually decided to take John Wycliffe in week 14 because he had helped pave the way for the Reformation. Jason announced with a grin that he'd take heresies in week 10, so that just left me. There were six topics left: the Anglo-Saxons, the Carolingians, the twelfth-century Renaissance, new religious orders, the late-medieval papacy, and a rather strange one titled 'A new beginning?' in the final week. I was dithering indecisively when Derek said that the

Carolingians were very interesting, so that settled it.

After Derek explained a few more details about tutorial papers, essays, and assessment in general we got ready to leave. Somehow or other, Frank and I happened to be the last to depart. Thought I noticed a zealous gleam in his eyes.

'*Now* I know why God wants me to study medieval church history!' he said excitedly.

'Oh, really?' I commented, not quite sure what to say.

'Yes ... I AM GOING TO CONVERT JASON!'

WEEK·TWO

The Franks

Maureen started this week's tutorial with a quick summary of the decline of the Roman Empire. To illustrate her main point she drew a rough map on the board.

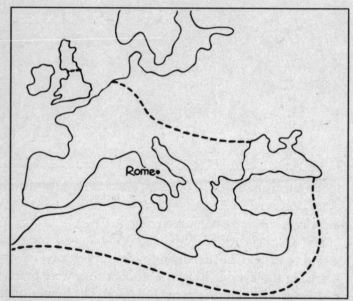

The late Roman Empire had an enormous border which stretched across Britain, France (Gaul), Germany, and eastern Europe; went down the Middle East; and then across north Africa. The cost of maintaining armies to defend the border was horrendous, and grew steadily worse as Germanic tribes pushed south from northern Europe. In the early fifth century the Ostrogoths, Visigoths and Vandals swept through the western part of the weakened empire and carved out territories for themselves in Italy, Spain and north Africa.

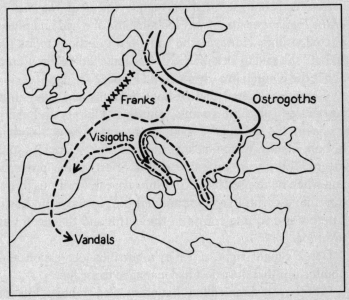

In the late fifth century it was the Franks' turn. They came to dominate most of Gaul, largely thanks to the outstanding military leadership of Clovis, who died in 511.

The Ostrogoths, Visigoths and Vandals had been converted to Arian Christianity in the fourth century. In other words, in the eyes of Roman Catholics they were heretics: they believed that Jesus was not fully God. The Franks, on the other hand, were pagans until Clovis converted to Catholicism in about AD 496. The Gallo-Roman aristocracy decided that a Catholic barbarian ruler was infinitely preferable to an

Arian one, and tried to make the best of things. Clovis was dubbed 'the new Constantine', the saviour of the Western Church. Gregory of Tours wrote a book about him and his descendants which we were supposed to read for our tutorial. Gregory was Bishop of Tours from 573 to 594, and a member of the Gallo-Roman aristocracy.

Maureen confessed that she hadn't read all of *The History of the Franks* because it was too long and she had had unexpected visitors. However, she had a few questions to ask us. 'What,' she said to kick-off the discussion, 'had we discovered about the Church in early medieval France?'

'Gregory reckoned that Bishops Salonius and Sagittarius committed "physical assaults, murders, adultery and every crime in the calendar",' said Jason with relish. 'Another bishop, Cautinus, was nearly always drunk, avaricious and mean. The queen gave one of his priests some property and when he refused to let Cautinus have it, Cautinus threw him into a coffin in a crypt and left him to starve to death. There was a rotting corpse in the coffin and the smell was revolting.'

Derek caught sight of Kirsty's horrified expression and pointed out that the priest had managed to escape.

'Another bishop called Badegisil also robbed lots of people,' went on Jason cheerfully, 'and he had a wife who liked cutting off men's penises and burning women's genitals with white-hot metal plates!'

'I don't think that we need to discuss things like that,' said Melinda in shocked tones.

'It's history!' retorted Jason smugly.

'Not *Christian* history,' maintained Melinda firmly.

'I was talking about bishops – how more Christian can you get?'

'I do not regard them as true Christians,' pronounced

Melinda. 'I am afraid that they could not have had access to the Bible.'

'Gregory did!' said Jason. 'He was forever boring on about the Old and New Testaments. I skipped those bits.' Melinda refrained from further comment with visible effort.

'Of course, not all women were like Bade-thingy's wife,' intervened Christobel. 'Some were frightfully good. The wife of Bishop Namatius used to read stories from a book to men who were building a church so that they could depict them in frescoes (which, incidentally, shows that there *were* educated women in the early Middle Ages). Anyway, one day a poor man saw this lady reading outside the church, and, thinking that she was old and poor too, gave her a piece of bread. She could have been offended but instead she insisted on eating it instead of her normal food that day. Isn't that touching?'

'I didn't know that bishops could marry,' said Kirsty shyly.

'Married men could be ordained,' replied Derek. 'However, from about the . . . er . . . fourth century onward priests were expected to abstain from sexual intercourse with their wives the night before celebrating the Eucharist. But then it . . . er . . . became the custom for the Eucharist to be celebrated every day.'

'Poor guys,' said Jason with feeling.

'The so-called "Church Fathers", especially rotten old Jerome and Augustine, had the most appallingly unhealthy view of sexuality,' said Christobel. 'They thought that it was impure, and "one does not approach the altar and the consecrated vessels with soiled hands".'

'Which comes from pagan religions, not Christianity,' interjected Frank. 'The New Testament tells us that sexual love is honourable and pure between husband and wife. Hebrews 13:4 . . .'

'I liked Gregory's story about the priest Cato who almost

became a bishop,' remarked Ruth, in response to a despairing glance from Derek. 'Cato was apparently a very proud and often disagreeable man, but when his region was ravaged by plague he refused to flee. He kept celebrating mass and burying the dead until he himself died. Gregory concluded: "This priest was a person of great humanity and devoted to the poor. He was a proud man, it is true, but what he did at this moment excused everything."'

'Religious men and women were virtually the only people in early medieval society who upheld public morality, showed compassion and dispensed charity to the poor,' asserted Wade. 'There was certainly no social welfare system, like we have today.'

'I thought at first that it must have been exciting when Clovis became a Christian,' ventured Kirsty, 'but he didn't seem to change much.'

'He was just as violent and treacherous as before, running around knocking people on the head with his axe whenever he felt like it,' observed Jason cynically, 'but, like lots of people, he used religion to justify his actions. Listen to this:

"I find it hard to go on seeing these Arians occupy a part of Gaul," said Clovis to his ministers. "With God's help let us invade them. When we have beaten them we will take over their territory . . ."

'If you ask me, their land and wealth was all that he cared about in the first place.'

'He obviously was not properly converted,' exclaimed Melinda crossly. 'He never repented of his sins but said that he would believe in Jesus *if* he was victorious in a certain battle. After the battle was won he was baptized, and all his followers had to get baptized, too. However, you cannot bargain with God – or frighten or bully people into having true faith!'

'I'm sure that he eventually became a Christian because of the absolutely wonderful example of Clotild, his Christian wife,' contended Christobel. 'While he was still a pagan, Clotild had their baby son baptized, and when the baby died immediately afterwards Clovis was frightfully angry and completely turned off Christianity. You would have thought that Clotild would have been full of grief and fear, but she was amazingly noble and cried:

> I give thanks to Almighty God . . . who has not found me completely unworthy, for He has deigned to welcome to His kingdom a child conceived in my womb. I am not at all cast down in my mind because of what has happened, for I know that my child, who was called away from this world in his white baptismal robes, will be nurtured in the sight of God.'

'As a mother, I don't call that noble. I call it unnatural,' said Maureen bluntly.

'Frankish queens didn't specialize in maternal emotions,' said Jason with a snigger. 'One of Clovis's grandson's wives was so jealous of her daughter that she put her in a cart drawn by untamed bulls. As a result, the daughter fell off a bridge and drowned. On the other hand, Clovis's niece got so mad when her mother wouldn't let her live with her lover (who was a slave) that she put poison in the chalice: her mother dropped down dead at the altar! But I like the story about wicked Queen Fredegund best. She conned her daughter into bending over to look into a big chest full of jewels, and then slammed the lid down on her neck. The girl would have died if a servant hadn't screamed for help.'

'Someone should give a copy of *The History of the Franks* to

Queen Elizabeth,' commented Maureen, 'if she hasn't got one already. It might help her to know that nothing Charles, Di, Andy, Fergie, and all the rest of her family ever did could possibly compare with the royal scandals in sixth-century Gaul!'

'A lot of the violence and warfare was exacerbated by the Frankish custom of dividing a kingdom between all the king's sons at his death,' said Wade.

'Yes, Clovis left his kingdom to his four sons,' said Jason. 'When one of them died, one of the others killed his two nephews and married his sister-in-law so that he could increase his territory. He later had one of his own sons burnt alive after a family dispute. God knows how many other people he killed. But when he was dying from a fever, according to Gregory, he said: "Well! Would you believe it ? . . . What manner of king can be in charge of heaven, if he is prepared to finish off great monarchs like me in this fashion?" '

'Arrogant pig!' said Maureen forcefully.

'Gregory certainly presents a very entertaining and vivid account of the aristocracy in sixth-century France, but we should not forget the ordinary people of the time,' reminded Wade. 'Interminable feuds and civil wars among the royal family and the aristocracy devastated the countryside. Armed bands continually marched about, destroying crops, looting and killing anyone who got in their way. People lucky enough to survive those depredations easily fell victim to famine, floods, fires and epidemics. Travel, trade, towns and education (which had all flourished in Roman times) were badly affected . . .'

'Yes, it must have been a lousy time to be alive,' concluded Maureen, 'almost as bad as the twentieth century, and the Church suffered, too. When some lord or other was invading

Tours, his army not only ravaged the surrounding district, but burnt churches, killed clergy, raped nuns and stole church property. But we should get back to my questions. What did you make of Gregory's stories about saints, relics, miracles, and that kind of thing?'

'I couldn't believe that people could be so gullible,' said Jason. 'Can you imagine anyone being stupid enough to go into battle with the finger of some dead saint-person tied onto his hand so that he would be victorious? Or drinking water mixed with dust from a saint's tomb to cure an illness? Or, wait for this, writing a letter to a saint, and leaving a blank piece of paper on his tomb so that he could reply? Surprise, surprise, he didn't! And if there was an eclipse, or a comet was sighted in the sky, it naturally meant that a terrible calamity was about to take place!'

'We naturally regard the medieval obsession with the corpses of saints, and other superstitious beliefs, with distaste,' commented Melinda. 'However, primitive people always seem to require magical and superstitious belief systems. It clearly comes from not knowing the Bible.'

Frank seized the opportunity to expound on the gifts of the Spirit. 'Of course, miracles, healings, and what not can occur, like Gregory reckoned happened when people drank water mixed with dust from saints' tombs, but that's just because Jesus said that "if you have faith as small as a mustard seed, you can say to this mountain, 'Move from here to there', and it will move. Nothing will be impossible to you." We know that is because of the Holy Spirit, but people in the Middle Ages thought it was because of some saint or other. Actually, all Christians are saints . . .'

'I suppose that life was often so harsh in the medieval period that it is not surprising that people wanted to have special relationships with holy people who had already become members of the court of heaven,' put in Ruth quietly. 'Saints probably seemed more approachable than God, and they were thought to have the ability to intercede on behalf of those still confined to earth for forgiveness of sins, healing from sickness and protection from enemies. They also made very inspiring role models.'

'I can sort of understand people wanting to have saints look after them,' said Kirsty. 'I like to think that my grandmother, who died two years ago, sort of watches over me. Like it says somewhere in the Bible: we are "surrounded by a great cloud of witnesses". However, I can't understand why bits of saints' bodies were so important. It seems horrid to think of bodies being cut up, and bits of skin and bone taken off for people to carry around.'

'The physical remains (or relics) were a direct link between the people on earth and the saints in heaven,' explained Ruth. 'R. W. Southern says in his book *Western Society and the Church in the Middle Ages* (p. 31) that:

> Relics were the main channel through which supernatural power was available for the needs of ordinary life. Ordinary men could see and handle them, yet they belonged not to this transitory world but to eternity. On the Last Day they would be reclaimed by the saints and become an integral part of the kingdom of heaven.'

'Er . . . to put it another way, Ronald Finucane says in his book *Miracles and Pilgrims* that relics seemed to emit a kind of "holy radioactivity",' added Derek.

'Which was just a lot of superstitious nonsense,' scoffed Jason. 'Gregory, for example, thought that he was saved from drowning when his boat began to fill with water just because he was carrying some relics of St Martin of Tours. I suppose that if everyone wanted to take part of a saint with them when they went on a journey it's no wonder bodies got cut up. Bits and pieces would be easier to carry than a whole corpse, and there'd be more to go around.'

Kirsty shuddered.

'However, the main significance of relics was that they boosted the social status of bishops,' maintained Wade. 'Tours was particularly famous because it contained the tomb of St Martin, who was one of Gaul's premier saints. People would flock to visit the tomb, and donate money and possessions to St Martin's church. Gregory, as St Martin's official representative, would dispense prayers, charity, hospitality, advice and rebukes. It was certainly in his best interests to promote the saint's cult. On one occasion he warned one of the king's warriors who was attacking Tours that "he would do better to shake in fear before Saint Martin the Bishop, whose miraculous power only the day before had made paralysed limbs straight". The man ignored the warning and died shortly afterwards from jaundice. Gregory left his readers to draw the (to him) obvious conclusion.'

'There was so much social status and prestige at stake,' continued Jason, 'that before Gregory's time, when St Martin kicked the bucket in a village somewhere, men from Tours and Poitiers fought over who got to keep his body. The men from Tours waited until the men from Poitiers (who were guarding the corpse) fell asleep, and then they grabbed it, shoved it through a window, and ran!'

'Highly unedifying,' snapped Melinda.

Derek pointed out that we had run over time, and thanked us all for coming.

'I never thought that medieval church history would be such fun!' Jason exclaimed as we prepared to leave. 'I expected it to be really pious and boring, but it's not. I've decided to do my essay on saints and relics. They seem to be an important aspect of medieval history, and quite a few books have been written about them, full of all kinds of wacky stories.'

'I must organize a meeting with my E-Team,' said Melinda grimly, when Jason had gone.

I asked what an 'E-Team' was. Melinda explained that an evangelism team from her church takes a non-Christian like Jason to a neutral place like a coffee shop, asks him what he thinks would happen to him if he died that night, and then tells him about the seriousness of sin and its consequences: eternal damnation. The non-Christian is then encouraged to repent of his sins, believe in the Bible, join a home group, and go to church regularly. Melinda was quite confident that Jason could be rescued and reformed. I nodded uncomfortably. Couldn't bring myself to admit that I quite like him the way he is.

WEEK·THREE

The Anglo-Saxons

About the same time as the Franks were invading Gaul, Anglo-Saxon tribes from what is now Denmark and Germany were invading Britain. Britain had been an outpost of the Roman Empire from the first century, but by the early fifth century the Romans could no longer effectively control the island and Roman troops withdrew to try to defend what remained of the empire elsewhere. Left to the ravages of the Anglo-Saxons, the Celtic tribes of Britain fled to remote places like Wales and Cornwall. Their battles with the invaders inspired legends (King Arthur, etc.) but very little is known about them from more reliable historical sources. Ireland and Scotland, incidentally, had never been conquered by Rome. Celtic tribes known as the Scots lived in Ireland, while the Picts lived in Scotland. Very confusing.

For our tutorial today we were supposed to read Bede's *History of the English Church and People*. When we all got together, Derek asked if we had been able to spot any similarities or differences between Bede and Gregory of Tours.

'Gregory was a Gallo-Roman aristocrat who lived in sixth-century France,' enthused Christobel, 'and he was a frightfully important bishop. He was involved in secular politics, travelled a great deal, and entertained lots of important people in Tours, so he was personally involved in many of the incidents he wrote about and in a position to get lots of juicy gossip. Bede, on the other hand, was a saintly little monk, tucked away in a monastery in a remote corner of northern England in the late seventh and early eighth centuries. He never travelled much, but devoted himself to studying scripture, teaching and writing.'

'So you don't get court gossip, like wicked queens trying to throttle their daughters,' said Maureen in a rather disappointed tone.

'Bede does reveal that the king of the South Mercians, who became a Christian when he married a Christian princess, was later treacherously murdered by her,' pointed out Jason, 'but, unfortunately, he doesn't give the gruesome details.'

'That reminds me of what I thought was a similarity between medieval France and England,' exclaimed Maureen. 'All those piddly little kingdoms, and kings and princes forever fighting one another. There was a king of Kent, a king Northumbria, a king of . . .'

'But in Bede's lifetime the island was relatively peaceful,' interrupted Wade. 'He ends his history on a more positive note than Gregory of Tours, who can only see evidence of drought, epidemics and other disasters.'

'I was struck by how primitive people were in the Dark Ages,' announced Melinda. 'Gregory and Bede were both quite naïve and credulous. They relate tales of miracles as if they had actually happened.'

'But they had a different worldview to ours,' argued Ruth. 'We have grown up in a society which places great emphasis on materialism and rationalism, at the expense of supernatural forces like angels, demons and the Holy Spirit. It was the opposite in the medieval period! Most people seem to have had a far greater sense of the closeness between heaven and earth than now. I was impressed by Bede's scholarship. He not only names the sources of his miracle stories, but he reveals that he submitted his accounts to other people familiar with the oral tradition for verification. Above all, he does not highlight the wonderful or bizarre nature of a miracle simply for the sake of entertaining his readers. He regards miracles as signs of God's intervention in the affairs of men and women, and evidence of the ongoing presence and influence of saints.'

'And the miracle stories subtly reinforce his main themes,' added Wade. 'A classic example would be Augustine's confrontation with the British Christians. No one knows exactly when Christianity reached Britain but it must have been sometime during the Roman occupation. The isolated Britons then developed their own Christian traditions, as did the Celtic tribes in Ireland and Scotland. There were no great doctrinal differences between them and the Rome-dominated Church, but they celebrated Easter on a different date, had a much less centralized ecclesiastical hierarchy, and so on. Augustine was the Roman monk sent by Pope Gregory the Great to convert the pagan Anglo-Saxons in 596 (not to be confused with Augustine of Hippo, the famous theologian). Augustine the missionary became the first Archbishop of Canterbury, and he tried to assert his authority over the Britons. Bede, who was passionately pro-Roman, claims that he demonstrated his authority by giving sight to a blind man, but the Britons obstinately refused to recognize him as their archbishop, change their dating of Easter, or join his mission to the Anglo-Saxons. In another chapter, Bede reveals that Augustine's successor, Laurence, was just about to flee from England and a hostile pagan king when he was chastised by St Peter for his cowardice. When the king saw the marks of Peter's lash on Laurence's skin, he was converted. In Bede's history, the miraculous intervention of Peter is certainly presented to explain the king's conversion, but it also subtly underlines the link between Peter, the papacy and the English church.'

'Gregory clearly initiated the mission to Britain to increase the papacy's influence in western Europe,' began Melinda.

'Yeah, well, I'm no defender of the Roman Catholic Church,' interrupted Frank animatedly, 'but what all Christian churches need today is power evangelism. Jesus and his disciples didn't just go around teaching people creeds and setting a good example. They exorcised demons, healed the sick and raised the dead. That really got people's attention! The twentieth-century Pentecostal revival is showing that the same Holy Spirit who worked through the disciples is still around today. Like Jesus said: "I tell you the truth, anyone who has faith in me will do what I have been doing. He will do even greater things than these, because I am going to the Father."' (John 14:12)

'I think that we shouldn't need miraculous demonstrations of power, but simply accept what is taught in the Bible by faith,' said Melinda. 'And I am afraid that so many Pentecostal leaders have been discredited by financial and sexual scandals ...'

'Interestingly, Pope Gregory wrote a letter to Augustine after he heard of the success of his mission and the miracles he had performed,' commented Ruth. She read part of it out: ·

'My very dear brother, I hear that Almighty God has worked great wonders through you for the nation which he has chosen. Therefore let your feeling be one of fearful joy and joyful fear at God's heavenly gifts – joy that the souls of the English are being drawn through outward miracles to inward grace; fear lest the frail mind becomes proud because of these wonderful events. For when it receives public recognition, it is liable to fall through senseless conceit. We should remember how the disciples returned from their preaching full of joy, and said to their heavenly Master: "Lord, even the devils are subject unto us, through thy name." But they received the prompt rejoinder: "In this rejoice not. But rather rejoice because your names are written in heaven." '

Derek said that was a very good point to remember, and then observed that the Christian mission to the Anglo-Saxons was the overriding theme of Bede's *History of the English Church and People*. What else had we been able to find about the methods which the missionaries used?

'They were terribly primitive,' stated Melinda. 'When Augustine reached Kent in 597, he and his followers went to meet the king "carrying a silver cross as their standard and the likeness of our Lord and Saviour painted on a board". How dreadfully pagan! Then, when the Pope sent Augustine supplies for the English church, he dispatched "sacred vessels, altar coverings, church ornaments, vestments for priests and clergy, relics of the holy Apostles and martyrs, and many books". There is no mention of the Bible, which should be a missionary's most precious possession!'

'The "many books" doubtless included Bibles,' said Wade.

'Possibly,' conceded Melinda, 'but I think that the fact that the Bible was not specifically mentioned is a sad indication of the priorities of the medieval Church.'

'I thought that it was amazing that Pope Gregory was so interested in the mission to the English, at a time when he was personally unwell and Rome was constantly threatened by barbarian attacks and ravaged by disease and famine,' remarked Ruth thoughtfully. 'Even Bede commented that "while other popes devoted themselves to building churches and adorning them with gold and silver, Gregory's sole concern was to save souls". He seems to have been a very wise man. When Augustine wrote to tell him that he had noticed that Christian customs, especially the method of saying mass, differed in Gaul and Italy, Gregory replied that Augustine was to select whatever customs seemed "devout, religious and right" for the English church. The discovery that people from different cultures may require different forms of worship is not a totally modern innovation, contrary to what a lot of today's Christian's think!'

'Well, I was quite shocked by the extent to which Gregory was prepared to compromise with pagan religions,' declared Melinda. 'He decreed that temples of idols were not to be destroyed, but purified for Christian worship; and Christian festivals were to be substituted for pagan ones. We have seen in Third World countries how easily the Christian message can be diluted and distorted by pagan beliefs. New Christians must be made to realize that they have to totally renounce their pagan past.'

'Gregory's point was that you cannot wipe out centuries of paganism in five minutes!' said Wade, with more than a hint of exasperation in his voice.

'I agree with Melinda,' retorted Frank. 'Far too many liberal Christians today go on about "dialoguing" with other religions, respecting their traditions, and what not. But there can be no compromise because the bottom line is that Jesus said that "I am the way and the truth and the life. No one comes to the Father except through me."' (John 14:6)

'I totally disagree!' cried Christobel. 'We are all God's children, and there is a great deal of value in other religious traditions. However, to get back to Derek's question about the methods missionaries used, I was absolutely thrilled to discover the prominent role women played in evangelism. King Ethelbert of Kent married Bertha, a Christian Frankish princess, before Augustine's arrival in England, and their Christian daughter Ethelberga later married Edwin, the pagan king of the Northumbrians . . .'

'Yes, but Bertha didn't convert Ethelbert,' objected Jason, 'and the Pope wrote a letter to Ethelberga telling her to try harder because she had little success, too. However, I accept your point that women can influence their husbands. When King Redwald of the East Angles became a Christian in 627, his wife persuaded him to go back to paganism! But what no one has said yet is how important the religion of the secular ruler really was. If a king didn't at least tolerate Christianity, a missionary had a snowball's chance in hell of working in his kingdom. On the other hand, if a king did become a Christian, nearly everyone else in the kingdom usually had to get baptized as well. Then, if a Christian king was succeeded by a pagan king, the kingdom was pagan again before the Christian king was cold in his grave.'

Derek sadly acknowledged that there was a tendency for that to happen. The degree of acceptance of Christianity varied from area to area, and setbacks frequently occurred.

'And it was the same in Denmark and Norway in the ninth century,' continued Jason. 'King Harald of Denmark decided that he and the entire Danish army would be baptized after a bishop called Poppo carried a red-hot iron in his hand and showed the king that it did not burn him. Then Harald sent men throughout the whole kingdom, with orders that people were to be baptized or suffer severe punishment! Surprise, surprise, when Harald died, everyone returned to pagan sacrifices. King Olaf of Norway also became a Christian, and vowed to introduce Catholicism to Norway or die. To make sure he succeeded, people who refused to convert were killed, mutilated or driven out of the country. Temples and statues of pagan gods were destroyed, and hostages were taken to make sure no one recanted!'

'Forgive me if I am wrong, but I was under the impression

that we were supposed to be discussing Anglo-Saxon England,' said Melinda acidly.

'I'm sure what happened in Norway and Denmark would have happened in England as well,' retorted Jason.

'Kirsty, what did you . . . er . . . think about the methods the missionaries used?' asked Derek uneasily.

Kirsty blushed and said that she liked the story of Aidan best. Derek encouraged her to reveal why.

'He was a bishop from Iona,' she explained, 'which I think was a monastery which had been established by Celtic monks from Ireland in Scotland. Anyway, Aidan came to Northumbria and founded another monastery on an island called Lindisfarne, which he sort of used as a base for missions to the Anglo-Saxons. I wrote down what Bede said about him:

> The highest recommendation of his teaching to all was that he and his followers lived as they taught. He never sought or cared for any worldly possessions, and loved to give away to the poor who chanced to meet him whatever he received from kings or wealthy folk. Whether in town or country, he always travelled on foot unless compelled by necessity to ride; and whatever people he met on his walks, whether high or low, he stopped and spoke to them. If they were heathen, he urged them to be baptized; and if they were Christians, he strengthened their faith, and inspired them by word and deed to live a good life and to be generous to others.

'Clearly the Celtic monks preached Christianity while the Roman monks just preached Roman Catholicism,' observed Melinda.

'They are not necessarily different things,' said Ruth through clenched teeth. 'I actually thought that it was interesting that the first monk sent from Iona to evangelize the

Anglo-Saxons had little success and he returned home to report that he had been unable to teach anything to such "an ungovernable people of an obstinate and barbarous temperament". Aidan thought that he had been too severe on his ignorant hearers, and "should have followed the practice of the Apostles, and begun by giving them the milk of simpler teaching, and gradually nourished them with the word of God until they were capable of greater perfection and able to follow the loftier precepts of Christ".'

'Toward the middle of the seventh century the Roman mission was really flagging, and for a while it looked as though Lindisfarne would overtake Canterbury in importance,' observed Wade. 'It was a great centre of scholarship and spirituality, as the Irish strongly emphasized teaching and preaching, rather than creating an organized church structure like the Romans.'

'And they kept Easter on a different date,' added Jason, 'which caused lots of hassles. In one place a queen (following the Roman date) was fasting for Palm Sunday, while the king (influenced by the Irish) thought that it was Easter Sunday. That really stuffed up their celebrations! Eventually the king got sick of this and called a synod to resolve the issue. The Roman representative convinced him that Jesus had given Peter the keys to the kingdom of heaven, and he had passed his authority on to the Bishop of Rome, so that was that.'

'It wasn't just the primacy of Rome that turned the tide against the Irish dating of Easter,' murmured Derek. 'In Bede's opinion, it was . . . er . . . a case of the customs of the universal Church versus those of an isolated country which was then thought of as being at the end of the earth.'

'And I suspect that as western Europe had become so politically fragmented, the concept of religious universality would have really appealed to monks like Bede,' said Christobel.

'The Church kept alive part of the classical civilization of the Roman Empire. But what is really fascinatingly significant is that the synod was held at Whitby Abbey, which was a double house for monks and nuns run by AN ABBESS! Hilda was of royal birth and extremely well-educated. Bede says that kings and princes used to go to Whitby to ask for her advice, and her monks were so well taught that many went on to become priests, and five became bishops "of outstanding merit and holiness"! If only the Church had recognized then that women like Hilda were just as capable as men of assuming leadership roles, how much trauma Christian women would have been spared in the twentieth century!'

Ruth agreed. 'You know, I remember being taught at school that the early medieval period was called the "Dark Ages",' she said reflectively. 'But the more I study it, the less "dark" it seems! There was a real intellectual revival in seventh-century England. The Irish monks and nuns had a great role to play in that, of course. In addition, in 668–9 the Pope sent to Canterbury two scholars, Archbishop Theodore and Abbot Hadrian. They attracted a large number of students whom they taught sacred and secular literature, poetry and astronomy. Their travelling companion on the journey to England was Benedict Biscop, who became Bede's abbot. He taught his monks Greek, Latin, theology, astronomy, art and music. Inspired by this training, Bede went on to become the earliest, and, in many people's opinion, the greatest English historian. In his own day he was probably more famous for his commentaries on scripture. He was also very interested in mathematics and chronology, and he popularized the dating system based on the "annus domini".'

'But he totally misunderstood the Bible!' objected Melinda. 'He believed that people could earn their salvation through good deeds, and lose it through bad deeds. That was why he wrote in his book: "If history records good things of good men, the thoughtful hearer is encouraged to imitate what is good; or if it records evil of wicked men, the devout, religious listener or reader is encouraged to avoid all that is sinful and perverse . . ." However, the Bible quite clearly teaches that salvation is by faith alone. Fortunately, that was reaffirmed during the Reformation.'

'I suppose that the only way that priests, bishops and monks could stop barbarians being violent and horrible was by threatening them with eternal damnation if they were bad, and promising them eternal life if they were good,' said Maureen, considering this issue. 'When my kids were little, I was forever either threatening to smack them or offering them treats. There's nothing like a fly swot by the back door and a jar of lollies in the pantry for ensuring good discipline.'

Melinda didn't look too impressed by this argument.

Derek asked if there was anything else that anyone would like to say before we finished up.

'Merely, that I hope that this tutorial will encourage us all to think about the need for sound, biblically-based evangelism,' replied Melinda in a pious tone.

'Well, I can tell you how *not* to go about evangelism!' said Jason nastily. 'I was cornered in the refectory yesterday lunchtime by three self-righteous, upper-middle-class evangelicals: a future doctor, lawyer and banker. It was grossly unfair – three against one! I was trying to relax with my Coke and sausage roll, and they kept boring on about sin and hell and what would happen if I died that night. They were worse than Jehovah's Witnesses. When I could at last get a word in, I told the guy who was obviously the ringleader that he could either leave me alone or discover what it was like having a sausage roll stuck up his nostril. That settled them,' he concluded with a reminiscent grin.

Melinda glared at him, grabbed her bag and walked off, muttering something about having done her duty.

Frank stopped me on the way out. 'You can't argue someone like Jason into the Kingdom,' he whispered. 'I'm believing that he will come to my Prayer, Praise and Holy Power rally next month. What he really needs is to see some demons cast out and some sick people healed. That can't fail to make him want to get saved!'

WEEK·FOUR

The Carolingians

My turn to lead the tutorial, worst luck. Everyone arrived on time except Kirsty. We waited about five minutes but eventually had to start without her. I explained that Clovis's descendants (known as the Merovingians) seem to have run out of steam by the beginning of the eighth century and effective power had passed to the Carolingian family, who supposedly served the Merovingians as mayors of the palace – sort of like prime ministers. Charles Martel, the founder of the Carolingian dynasty, consolidated his position by defeating the Muslims who were attacking Gaul from the south (they had already conquered Spain), and the pagan Saxons who were proving troublesome in the north.

Charles's son Pippin was also a successful military leader, and in 750 he sent envoys to Rome to ask the Pope whether it was right that a man who had no power should be called king. Pope Zacharias replied: 'It is better to give the title of king to the one who holds the power.' Pippin promptly deposed the last Merovingian king and had himself crowned by Boniface, an Anglo-Saxon missionary.

Pippin's son Charles was even more successful. He has gone down in history as Charlemagne, or Charles the Great. The territories he conquered included most of what is now Germany, Austria, Switzerland, Italy, Holland and Belgium.

In Rome, on Christmas Day in the year 800, Pope Leo III crowned him emperor.

'What', I asked to encourage discussion, 'do you think about the relationship between the papacy and the Carolingians?'

'Obviously, Pippin and Charlemagne both used stupid old popes to further their own ends,' scoffed Jason. 'They had to legitimize their rule somehow, and the Pope could give a convenient spiritual blessing.'

'On the contrary,' said Melinda firmly, 'successive popes tried to use Pippin and Charlemagne for their own advantage. You must remember the situation confronting the papacy in the eighth century. The emperor of the remnant of the Roman Empire, which was centred on Constantinople (now, I think, known as the Byzantine Empire), condemned the use of images in religious worship (quite rightly, too, because they are clearly prohibited in the Bible). However, the Pope supported their use (the West was so terribly primitive). The emperor, in response, confiscated papal estates in southern Italy and removed Greek churches from the Pope's jurisdiction. He even sent soldiers to arrest the Pope but they were shipwrecked and couldn't fulfil their commission.'

'What a pity,' muttered Frank.

'In view of these events,' continued Melinda, 'the Pope wanted to free himself from ties to the Byzantine Empire and establish an autonomous papal state in Italy. As the barbarian Lombards were continually threatening to invade Rome, this was a seemingly impossible undertaking until Pippin's envoys appeared on the scene. The Pope seized the opportunity to do Pippin a favour, by supporting his *coup d'état*, and, in return, he exacted a promise that Pippin would restore to St Peter land supposedly stolen by the Lombards. In fact, the Pope's claim to these lands was based on a document known as the "Donation of Constantine", which was a flagrant forgery.'

Wade nodded, and explained that the 'Donation' claims that when Constantine travelled east and made Constantinople his capital, he gave the Pope dominion over 'the city of Rome and all the provinces, districts and cities of Italy and the Western regions'. Historians disagree over when exactly the document was composed, but, in Wade's opinion, it undoubtedly arose some time during the eighth century when the papacy was trying to extend its territory.

'Quite scandalous!' exclaimed Melinda. 'It clearly shows the extent to which the medieval Church had declined.'

'Er . . . forgery certainly seems reprehensible to us,' intervened Derek, 'but it was not uncommon in the medieval period, and perhaps not . . . er . . . regarded so harshly. If a church or monastery, or even the papacy, genuinely believed that it was entitled to some rights or possessions, but the charters supporting the claim had been lost due to fire, flood, vandalism or simply the passing of time, new charters were composed and . . . er . . . backdated.'

'Be that as it may, the "Donation" seems more like a fairy tale than a genuine historical charter,' said Wade. 'Its account of Constantine's conversion, after he was cured of leprosy by St Peter, was never mentioned in any early Church history book I ever read.'

'It was clearly written to take advantage of the ridiculous veneration of Peter that was encouraged by the medieval Church,' declared Melinda. 'Pippin was convinced that the only way that he could please Peter (who had the keys to the kingdom of heaven) was by conquering the Lombards and handing their territory to the Pope. And that was the beginning of the papal state which existed in Italy until 1870.'

'I didn't get the impression that Pippin was all that devout,' said Maureen brusquely. 'Whatever the Pope's motives were in making Pippin king, I reckon he came off worst from the deal. Pippin dominated the church in France, and Charlemagne later took control of the church in Germany and Italy as well.'

'This raises a very important issue in the history of Church–State relations,' commented Derek. 'What . . . er . . . is the role of a "Christian" State with regard to the Church? Is the State the protector of the Church, and if so, is the . . . er . . . Head of State ultimately subordinate to the head of the Church? In other words, should he act at the Pope's direction to govern Christian society and defend the Church from attack? Or is the Head of State an autonomous ruler who . . . er . . . acts on his own initiative and is responsible to God alone?'

'The papal view was obviously that the State was subordinate to the Church, and the Carolingians thought the opposite,' said Wade. 'Clearly, as the Carolingians had the most wealth and power, their view prevailed.'

'I read that one of the great weaknesses of the Merovingians was their lack of wealth,' put in Ruth, 'and a medieval ruler without sufficient land to reward his followers was in a very vulnerable position. When Pippin came to power he solved that problem by seizing Church property.'

'The Church should not have owned so much land in the first place,' maintained Melinda, 'and Pippin did legislate to ensure that everyone paid tithes to support the clergy. I was also pleased to see that he encouraged evangelism.'

'In territories he was trying to conquer,' said Jason sarcastically. ' "Spreading the Gospel" provided a great excuse for attacking pagans. The Bible and the sword went hand in hand. In 777 the death penalty was decreed for anyone who opposed conversion. Then, when land was overtaken, Frankish churches and monasteries were set up to subdue the conquered people, to teach them that "good Christians" didn't revolt against their masters, and so on.'

'I think that that kind of mission is absolutely awful,' cried Christobel, 'and I don't like the way Pippin and Charlemagne made the clergy swear allegiance to them, either. Bishops and abbots also had to supply men for their armies, just like secular lords. It was a frightful mingling of Church and State.'

'The bishops and abbots often *were* secular lords, or their sons,' added Wade. 'And they were generally appointed by the king.'

'They were certainly used as government officials, envoys on diplomatic missions, and that kind of thing,' remarked Ruth. I suppose that very few people outside the Church would have been able to read and write enough to draft and copy government letters and other documents.'

'Er . . . although I raised the issue of Church–State relations earlier, I really should qualify what I said by adding that there was no real distinction between "Church" and "State" in this period,' intervened Derek. 'Kings were thought to rule by the grace of God within, not outside the Church. They were seen as . . . er . . . God's agent for maintaining peace and order . . .'

'So they could interfere in practically every aspect of church life,' said Maureen. 'That's what really stuck in my gullet. Pippin and Charlemagne called church councils, took charge of debates and tried to enforce their decrees.'

'They both attempted to reorganize the Church, which was sadly in need of reform,' interrupted Melinda, 'but I was very sorry to see that they were greatly influenced by the Roman Church. The main purpose of their legislation was to bring the Frankish church into conformity with Rome.'

'Which again probably indicates the great esteem in which St Peter was held in the Middle Ages,' said Ruth quietly.

'Actually, I thought the Frankish church was frightfully

Old Testamentish,' said Christobel with an airy gesture. 'All that emphasis on divine kingship – and so little attention paid to the New Testament teaching on humility, love and service!'

'What's wrong with the Old Testament?' asked Frank. 'And Paul did say in Romans 13:1: "Everyone must submit himself to the governing authorities, for there is no authority except that which God has established. The authorities that exist have been established by God."'

'So God established Hitler!' said Jason with a malicious smile.

'Of course he didn't,' intervened Maureen heatedly, 'but I bet some German Christians used that verse as an excuse for not doing anything to stop him. If you ask me, Christians are often their own worst enemies. Charlemagne's clerical advisers went on and on, blabbing about how wonderful he was, and how he had been chosen by God to rule the "Christian Empire". Someone even said that he was the "vicar of God", and on him "rested the whole salvation of the Church of Christ". No wonder he became an ego-maniac with dozens of wives and mistresses . . .'

I quickly asked another one of my questions: 'Who do you think instigated the coronation of Charlemagne in AD 800?'

'It quite clearly must have been the Pope,' stated Melinda emphatically. 'By 799 Leo III was politically and morally discredited. He was almost overthrown by a conspiracy . . .'

'He was attacked and beaten up by men who tried to tear out his tongue and gouge out his eyes,' said Jason in an enthusiastic tone.

Melinda looked at him with disgust.

'And', she continued curtly, 'he was accused of perjury and adultery. According to Ullmann, in his *Short History of the Papacy in the Middle Ages*, Leo was "extremely alert, realistic and perceptive". He seized the opportunity afforded by troubles in Constantinople . . .'

'Emperor Constantine VI's mother had deposed and blinded him, and taken over the throne herself,' Jason interrupted again, 'which many people thought wasn't right because she was a woman.'

'And WHY shouldn't a WOMAN be emperor?' demanded Christobel. 'Irene was a very capable ruler, far more so than her son. And it is by no means clear what her role in his blinding actually was. I cannot imagine how a mother could possibly allow such a horrific thing to happen. It must have been done without her permission.'

'Oh, it was quite common in those days,' said Jason. 'Constantine himself had one of his uncle's eyes put out and the tongues of four more slit to eliminate them as possible rivals to the throne . . .'

'If I may be allowed to continue,' said Melinda, 'I would like to point out that Leo crowned Charlemagne emperor . . .'

'To thumb his nose at Constantinople . . .'

'To demonstrate his independence from Constantinople,' battled on Melinda, resolutely trying to ignore Jason, 'and provide himself with a secular protector to subdue the unruly Roman citizens.'

Wade, however, looked sceptical.

'I cannot believe the traditional story that Charlemagne had no idea that the Pope was going to crown him when he went to mass on Christmas Day,' he remarked. 'Leo was a weak character, publicly humiliated, and totally dependent on Charlemagne for survival. Charlemagne was clearly the most powerful ruler in the West, far more significant than a mere king. Being crowned "emperor" only made official what was *de facto* the case. The sole difference it seems to have made to him was that it confirmed his belief that he could take charge of the Roman Church. He had warned Leo, when Leo was elected in 795, that the Pope should confine himself to prayer and let the secular ruler do everything else. Now he proceeded to demonstrate his authority. I fail to see what Leo could possibly have hoped to gain if he had instigated the coronation.'

'I still think Charlemagne's clerical advisers have a lot to answer for,' observed Maureen again. 'They filled him up with ideas that he was just like King David, ruling a Christian empire, with a duty to protect the faith and the Church . . .'

'You would have thought that he would have been too busy with his wars and his mistresses to worry about religion,' sniggered Jason.

'I am afraid that his religion was very crude,' acknowledged Melinda disapprovingly. 'He was very interested in astrology, and he encouraged the veneration of saints.'

'He even had cavities built into his throne to hold relics,' said Jason. 'Fancy sitting on the remains of a mouldy old saint! I don't know whether Charlemagne had them or not, but some medieval rulers even had relics put in their crowns and strung around their necks. I suppose that if relics were thought to emit "holy radioactivity" the king wanted to make sure that he got the greatest zap.'

'Michael, have you got any more questions that you would like to ask?' inquired Derek.

I said that I wondered what the group had been able to find out about something called the 'Carolingian Renaissance'.

'I always thought that the Renaissance was the fifteenth-century revival of art and literature which followed the cultural decline of the Middle Ages,' answered Melinda. 'I cannot see that the eighth century witnessed anything remotely as significant.'

'Didn't we briefly consider the Anglo-Irish revival of

scholarship last week?' asked Ruth politely. 'Anglo-Irish missionaries spread the revival to the Continent. Several scholars, most notably Alcuin, became prominent men at Charlemagne's court.'

'Alcuin! That was the name of the monk from York who raved on about Charlemagne being just like David, the vicar of God, and all that rubbish,' exclaimed Maureen, looking pleased. 'Isn't it frustrating when you can't remember names?'

'Naturally, I don't agree with all that imperial ideology,' interjected Christobel, 'but one of the few good things that Charlemagne did was to insist that churches and monasteries had to have schools attached to them to train clergy and copy manuscripts. Education is so terribly important. And Charlemagne encouraged Alcuin to produce a revised and corrected version of the Bible, which was frightfully necessary because over the years different copyists had made all kinds of mistakes.

Melinda conceded that that aspect of the Carolingian Renaissance had been worthwhile.

'But Charlemagne didn't encourage scholarship for scholarship's sake,' protested Wade. 'It was simply a means to an end for him: the end being an educated clergy to convert and pacify his subjects. And he certainly didn't promote creative and innovative thinking. The whole emphasis of the Carolingian Renaissance was on standardization and systemization.'

I managed to read out five points I had noted with regard to the Carolingian Renaissance:

1 It attracted scholars from all over Europe;
2 Books were exchanged and copied, and rare manuscripts preserved;
3 A new kind of script was developed to make manuscripts more legible;

4 The Christian dating system was adopted; and
5 Education was seen as necessary for the moral rejuvenation of the community.

'Regrettably, Charlemagne was far too influenced by the Roman Catholic Church's ritualism and legalism,' maintained Melinda. 'I fail to see what good education did the clergy. They mumbled mass in Latin with their backs to the people, who generally couldn't hear or understand what they were saying. I couldn't find any evidence of sound, biblical preaching . . .'

At this point Kirsty arrived, looking very hot and hassled. She apologized for being late. She had missed her bus and had had to walk most of the way.

'What can we conclude about this topic?' asked Derek, with something that looked like a wink in my direction. 'Who thinks that the Pope . . . er . . . instigated Charlemagne's coronation?' Melinda and Frank put up their hands.

'Who thinks Charlemagne was . . . er . . . responsible?' Christobel said 'absolutely' and Wade agreed.

'Who blames Charlemagne's advisers?' Maureen waved both arms in the air.

'And who . . . er . . . thinks that the Pope, Charlemagne and his advisers could all have been involved, to a greater or lesser degree?' Ruth raised her hand, so I did too.

'And what about you, Jason?' asked Derek.

'I couldn't care less,' said Jason frankly. 'Why does it matter? Charlemagne's last years were spent frantically trying to keep his empire together, and it collapsed pretty soon after he died.'

'What else could you expect in the Dark Ages?' concluded Melinda.

Took Kirsty to the refectory to buy her a drink. Boy, am I glad that ordeal's over!

WEEK·FIVE

Monasticism

Ruth very capably led the tutorial. She started with a brief discussion about the Benedictine Rule, which, she said, ranks as one of the most influential documents ever written. It is the basis for one of the longest surviving forms of Christian commitment, and one of the most enduringly important schools of Christian spirituality. It is, of course, attributed to St Benedict, who lived in sixth-century Italy.

'It used to be assumed that the Rule was an original work,' put in Wade knowledgeably, 'but most scholars now believe that Benedict copied large sections of it from an earlier rule, known as the Rule of the Master.'

Having gained the impression from university that 'Thou shalt not Plagiarize' should be the eleventh commandment (if not a criminal offence), this was rather perturbing.

Ruth, however, was not fazed. 'Dozens of rules were drawn up in the early medieval period for individual religious houses,' she responded, 'and they drew on well-developed Western monastic traditions. The Benedictine Rule is no exception. What is remarkable about it, I think, is its simplicity and moderation. The Rule of the Master is so long and detailed that it even contains regulations for blowing your nose! St Benedict, in contrast, tried to develop a "very little rule for beginners" which contained "nothing harsh or burdensome".'

'Well, if that's his idea of a rule for beginners, I sure am glad he never devised one for advanced monks,' declared Maureen. 'They were supposed to keep silent almost all of the time, which would have driven me mad. Since my divorce I've learnt to cope with poverty and celibacy; it's living alone and not having anyone to talk to for hours at a stretch that really gets me down. But', she added on a determinedly more cheerful note, 'my kids gave me a parrot for my birthday, and it said its first words the other day.'

Christobel, with a concerned expression on her face, asked what these were.

'Bloody men,' replied Maureen.

While Christobel insisted that Maureen ring her absolutely any time that she was feeling lonely, Ruth asked Kirsty what had struck her most about the Benedictine Rule. Kirsty thought it was the fact that monks weren't allowed to have any personal possessions whatsoever, and they were only supposed to be provided with very simple food and clothes.

'What? No CD players, video recorders or motorbikes?' cried Jason. 'Life wouldn't have been worth living!'

'As a matter of fact,' intervened Melinda dourly, 'peasants who joined monastic communities in the Dark Ages wouldn't have had much to give up. They were probably considerably better off in a monastery, where they at least received decent clothing and regular meals. And whatever Benedict's original intentions, monasteries soon became wealthy and corrupt. Members of the nobility who became monks and nuns continued to live very comfortable lives.'

'That did happen at some houses. Others remained very poor,' said Ruth. 'As Tellenbach remarks in *The Church in Western Europe from the Tenth to the Early Twelfth Century* (p. 102), one of the most remarkable phenomena in history is the fact that the men and women who enjoyed the greatest wealth and prestige in medieval society were the most likely to renounce earthly pleasures and join religious communities. Michael, what feature of monastic life do you think was the most significant?'

I said something about monks spending an awful lot of time praying. They had to go to church seven times a day, and once in the middle of the night. I didn't say what I was really thinking: that I sometimes find it a struggle to get to church once a week. Maureen was more honest, and confided that now she came to think about it, going to church so often was probably worse than not being allowed to talk.

'There was a great deal of unnecessary ritualism and legalism,' remarked Melinda. 'It was quite unbiblical.'

'My Christian fellowship doesn't believe in following a set liturgy or lectionary,' said Frank. 'We let ourselves be led by the Holy Spirit.'

'According to Pope Gregory the Great, St Benedict had the gift of prophecy and performed many miracles,' countered Ruth. 'However, he believed that self-discipline would help spiritual progress.'

'Self-discipline is one thing, but we are all individuals with different needs, and I think that Benedict overdid his emphasis on monks obeying their abbot,' said Christobel. 'They were supposed to do absolutely everything the abbot commanded, without murmuring or delay. I know that this was supposed to make them frightfully humble . . .'

'It would have driven me up the wall,' said Maureen frankly, 'and encouraged the abbot to be a real autocrat.'

'Benedict hoped that abbots would be devoted, wise and loving fathers to their monks,' pointed out Ruth, 'and he warned them that they would have to account for their monks' souls on Judgement Day.'

'However,' declared Wade, 'a fundamental weakness of monasticism was the fact that a life of humility and obedience as a monk was very poor training for the role of abbot. Medieval abbots were often responsible for large communities and estates, and, like secular lords, they were required to play a considerable role in the economic, political and military affairs of their regions. Not infrequently, a saintly monk proved to be an incompetent administrator, while a good administrator tended to become secularized and removed from the spiritual life of his monastery. Sometimes a layman was even appointed abbot, and his monastic duties were delegated to a subordinate. In any case, the abbot enjoyed almost absolute security of tenure. He could not be dismissed unless he was found guilty of very serious faults, and he could not be forced to resign if he became too old or sick to rule properly.'

'I've known Protestant ministers who could preach good sermons and conduct nice funerals,' reflected Maureen, 'but they couldn't organize their way out of a paper bag. Fortunately, they always seemed to have super-efficient wives who managed to get them wherever they had to be on time. I've often wondered how Catholic priests cope.'

'Some have religious sisters and other lay people working as pastoral associates,' said Ruth dryly. 'Has anyone anything else that they would like to say about the Benedictine Rule?'

'Monks didn't seem to have any privacy in their monastery,' observed Kirsty, 'and they weren't supposed to go outside it. Couldn't they even spend holidays with their families?'

'St Benedict certainly didn't envisage monks going on any kind of holiday,' replied Ruth. 'As time went on, it became customary for them to visit their parents when their parents were on their deathbeds, and I think that in the late Middle Ages Benedictine monks were allowed to have a week or so with their families once a year. But, although Benedict's insistence on stability may seem harsh to us, remember that he lived during the time of the barbarian invasions. The world must have seemed a very violent and chaotic place, and travel was very difficult and dangerous.'

'Nevertheless,' said Melinda, 'shutting oneself in a monastery is quite contrary to the great commission in the Bible: "Go and make disciples of all nations." We are called to be evangelists, not to try to earn our own salvation through Pharisaic-type fasting and praying.'

Frank agreed.

'Although monks and nuns were not usually expected to take part in the . . . er . . . *vita activa* (pastoral work, evangelism, and so on), they were not restricted to just seeking their own salvation,' intervened Derek earnestly. 'They . . . er . . . prayed for people outside the monastery, that they would experience peace and prosperity and the salvation of their souls . . .'

Ruth nodded. 'And Benedictine monasticism was not, of course, the only form of monastic life in early medieval Europe. What can you remember about the Celtic monks of Ireland?' she asked.

'The Celts tended to be very individualistic and austere,' answered Wade. 'As part of their ascetic ideal they sought exile from home and family for the sake of Christ: "Foxes have holes and birds of the air have nests, but the son of Man has no place to lay his head", and so on. They were also strongly evangelical, and they used their self-imposed exile to convert pagan tribes to Christianity. They wandered around England, converting the Anglo-Saxons, and then went on to Europe. Wherever they went, they established monasteries as bases for evangelism.'

Ruth then revealed that a great wave of Irish monk-missionaries travelled to the Continent between the seventh and ninth centuries. Among other things, they spread the Irish emphasis on self-sacrifice, the independence of monasteries from bishops, the study of scripture, pastoral work, the practice of personal confession of sins, and the use of penitential books with prescribed lists of penances.

'I had a friend once who was an Irish Catholic,' said Maureen, 'and she was forever going off to confession on Saturday morning to confess that she'd eaten a lamb chop on Friday, or missed mass on Sunday, or some other trivial thing that really seemed to bother her. Hearing her talk used to make me glad that I wasn't Catholic. You wouldn't get me lining up to go into a booth to tell my sins to a MAN.'

'In some cases confessing one's faults and then being assured of God's forgiveness can be quite therapeutic,' responded Christobel, reaching out her hand to touch Maureen, 'but I think it is far better for women to share their experiences with a supportive network of women friends. And I am totally against the mechanical listing of sins and penances. St Columban, who set up a monastery in Gaul in about 590, made his monks confess their faults twice a day. They then had to receive a fixed number of slaps: up to a dozen if they forgot to say grace before a meal or laughed during prayers, and fifty for telling idle stories or shouting loudly. What a dismal place that monastery must have been! God wants us to enjoy life, not get paranoid about perceived misdemeanours. But medieval monks did, which I think was a frightfully unhealthy aspect of monasticism, and one which was passed on to the modern Church.'

Ruth agreed, but mentioned that in recent years more emphasis has been placed on reconciliation than penance.

'Were there any Irish nun-missionaries?' asked Kirsty.

'None that I know of,' said Christobel regretfully, 'but that could be because male historians didn't bother to write about them, or it wasn't considered suitable for women to journey about evangelizing at that time. However, Bede does reveal that there were the most amazing Anglo-Saxon nuns in the seventh and eighth centuries: women like Hilda, the niece of the king of Northumbria who became Abbess of Whitby. Even Bede admits that Whitby was a wonderful centre of holiness and spirituality. And he also writes about Queen Etheldreda who was married twice but refused to consummate her marriages and eventually became Abbess of Ely.'

'She was the one whose body was dug up sixteen years after she was buried so that it could be transferred to another place,' said Jason with a grin, 'and it was found to have been miraculously preserved from decay. She looked even better than on the day she died, which, Bede says, was evidence that she had remained untainted by sexual intercourse!'

'Stories of saints' bodies remaining uncorrupted or emitting pleasant odours are quite common in medieval literature,' remarked Wade coolly. 'Although attributed to divine intervention, if such "miracles" did take place it was doubtless a result of embalming or the transformation, in damp, airtight conditions, of body fat to a waxy substance which doesn't deteriorate easily.'

'The missions of the Celtic monks of Ireland and the Benedictine monks sent to England by Pope Gregory the Great fused at the Synod of Whitby in 664,' went on Ruth. 'Anglo-Saxon missionaries then played a vital role in converting pagan tribes on the Continent. The most famous monk-missionary is probably St Boniface, who is known as the Apostle to the Germans. He combined the Irish love of evangelism with Roman organizational skills and loyalty to the papacy. He founded many Benedictine monasteries in

Germany before being martyred in 754.'

'Wasn't he the one who cut down an oak tree which the pagans thought was sacred?' said Frank in a pleased voice. 'Used its wood to build a church. Ha ha.'

'Then I don't blame the pagans for bumping him off,' commented Jason. 'But he didn't just cut the tree down. He accepted Frankish military support to further his missions, helped dethrone the last Merovingian king and crown Pippin, and was a key factor in cementing the alliance between the papacy and the Carolingians.'

'I am not at all sure that that was a good thing,' observed Christobel, 'but what is really thrilling is that he asked his cousin Lioba, an Anglo-Saxon nun, to assist his missionary work. Lioba established lots of religious communities for women, which also followed the Benedictine Rule. The nuns farmed their land, taught, cared for the sick, provided hospitality to travellers, wrote books and copied manuscripts. Lioba herself was frightfully well-educated, and it was said that she was never without a book by her. She was also a great friend of Charlemagne's wife Hildegard. Her biographer wrote that, although she did not like the hectic atmosphere of the royal court, she would sometimes go to visit Hildegard. All the princes, nobles and bishops loved her and welcomed her with joy, and because of her wisdom and great knowledge of scripture they would ask her advice and discuss spiritual and ecclesiastical matters with her.'

Ruth agreed with Christobel that Lioba was a very inspiring example of a religious woman, and although we might have qualms about some aspects of their alliance with the Carolingians, Lioba and Boniface helped reform the Frankish church and paved the way for the Carolingian Renaissance which we considered last week.

'Charlemagne typically wanted to ensure that all

monasteries in his empire followed the same rule,' said Wade. 'He supported the use of the Benedictine Rule, and, after his death in 814, his son Louis the Pious authorized Benedict of Aniane to enforce the observance of his version of the Rule throughout France and Germany.'

'Then monastic life declined,' asserted Melinda. 'Monasteries became far too wealthy and linked to the nobility. They were spiritually lax but economically and politically important . . .'

'Well, they didn't stay important for long,' interrupted Jason. 'The Carolingian empire was too large to be effectively governed, and in the ninth century Charlemagne's grandsons tore it apart with civil wars. Then there was another wave of invasions: Vikings from the north, Muslims from the south, and Magyars or Hungarians from the east. Western European "civilization" almost totally collapsed, and many monasteries were plundered and destroyed.'

'That's when the feudal system developed,' said Maureen knowingly. 'As the central government was stuffed, monasteries needed secular warriors to protect them from enemy raids. Fortunately, warriors wanted monasteries to pray for them, so they did a deal. And both lots had to have serfs to work their land. Career choices were pretty limited. If you were a man, you either fought, prayed or worked. And as usual it was worse for women: you either married or went into a convent. Some choice!'

'The . . . er . . . traditional distinction between those who prayed, those who fought and those who worked is a bit . . . er . . . over-simplified,' intervened Derek as gently as possible so that he did not hurt Maureen's feelings. 'Many monks and rural clergy engaged in manual labour, while some bishops and abbots behaved rather like warriors, and it is to be hoped that everyone prayed sometimes. Also, while . . . er . . . some areas were certainly devastated by raids, many were relatively unaffected . . .'

'Yes,' said Ruth reflectively, 'but the impression I got from my reading was that there was a great deal of instability. Even if people lived in areas which were not directly threatened by the Vikings, Magyars or Muslims, they could still suffer from disputes and petty wars between noble families, and death from violence or disease must have been much more common than today. The fact that the world was such a dangerous place seems to have encouraged people to turn to recognized holy men and holy places for protection and inter-cession.'

'You mean they tried to buy protection and salvation by giving gifts to monasteries,' said Frank in an aggressive tone, 'which was not biblical.'

'And monasteries, in turn, tried to ensure their own protec-tion and well-being by having a patron saint or two on hand,' added Jason. 'Even if the saints' intercessions in heaven didn't help, the gifts left by credulous pilgrims certainly did. There are lots of stories about monasteries who didn't have popular saints' relics pinching some from others which did. Of course, this was only done after the saint appeared in a vision to the thief to tell him that he was unhappy where he was and would really like to move to the thief's house . . .'

Melinda raised her eyes to the ceiling.

'In the tenth century reform movements sprang up in monasteries throughout Europe,' said Ruth. 'Now, this does not necessarily mean that existing monasteries were lax or corrupt.' Melinda, Jason, Wade and Frank looked sceptical. 'Rather,' continued Ruth, 'there was great interest in estab-lishing or re-dash-forming monasteries according to new interpretations of the Benedictine Rule. The most famous reform movement arose in Burgundy. Cluny was founded by the Duke of Aquitaine in 910. According to its foundation charter, no bishop or lord was to interfere in the internal affairs of the abbey. It was to be dependent on the Pope alone, but as he was far away it was virtually left to its own devices. In Cluny's case this turned out to be a very good thing, because it had a series of holy, zealous and long-lived abbots. They took very seriously their responsibility to pray for secular benefactors and society as a whole. In fact, Morris in *The Papal Monarchy* (p. 65) describes Cluny as a "power-house of prayer".'

'According to the original Benedictine Rule, a monk's day was carefully balanced, with almost equal time devoted to communal worship, private prayer and study, and manual labour,' remarked Wade. 'However, the liturgy at Cluny occupied almost the entire day. There was no time for physical labour and precious little time for study or anything else.'

'How awful,' said Maureen, 'and very unhealthy, being shut up in church all day and night.'

'I suppose it really impressed warriors who visited the abbey,' mused Christobel. 'After all, if you were going to donate lots of money to a monastery, it was nice to know that the monks would be continually praying for you and your family.'

'So the Cluniac reform became very popular and spread throughout Europe,' concluded Ruth. 'Lots of nobles who had ruined monasteries on their estates, or ones which followed a different way of life, asked the Abbot of Cluny to send some of his monks to re-dash-form their monasteries.'

'I bet that wasn't popular with all the old monks,' said Jason, 'especially as Cluny developed a highly centralized administrative system. There was only one abbot, the Abbot of Cluny, and all "daughter" priories were supposed to obey the "mother" house.'

'I don't think that Cluny's order was ever as centralized as the later Cistercian Order,' put in Derek. 'Cluny's *Ordo* was much more a way of life adopted by other houses than an institution. Some . . . er . . . "daughter" houses were certainly under the authority of the Abbot of Cluny, but others adopted the Cluniac lifestyle while remaining substantially independent.'

'I am afraid that as a result of their popularity, Cluniac monasteries became very wealthy,' claimed Melinda. 'Their buildings, especially their churches, were excessively elaborate, abbots were overly concerned with worldly affairs, and discipline grew lax.'

'Those accusations were made against Cluny in the eleventh and twelfth centuries,' admitted Ruth, 'but how fair they were is another matter. It is worth noting that Cluniac monks continued to be held in very high regard by bishops, popes, nobles and emperors throughout the medieval period. Yet, partly in reaction to Cluny, other forms of religious life emerged in the eleventh and twelfth centuries which placed greater emphasis than Cluny on simplicity, poverty, and so on. We will be looking at those in a few weeks' time so I won't say anything more about that now. Has anyone got anything else they would like to contribute today?'

'She wasn't a Cluniac nun but I just have to mention Hrotsvit of Gandersheim,' said Christobel. 'She actually lived in the tenth century, about the time that Cluny was taking off. Gandersheim had been founded in 852 for daughters of the Saxon aristocracy. They followed the Benedictine Rule more or less – they had to strictly observe celibacy, obedience and the times for worship but they didn't have to take a vow of poverty. Amazingly, in 947 the German king Otto I freed the abbey from royal control and gave the abbess the authority to have her own army and court of law! She could even mint her own coins and sit in the imperial diet! At the time, Gandersheim must have been a great intellectual centre, with a school and a library which contained a great number of medieval and ancient classics. Encouraged by her abbess, Hrotsvit made the most of her education and talent for writing and composed the first known Christian dramas, the first known Saxon poetry, and the first known German history! Funnily enough, in her plays women are nearly always the Christian heroines, while the pagans are horrible men:

Diocletian: For her speech so brazen, to the tortures she must be taken.
Hirena: That is just what we hope for, that is what we desire, that for the love of Christ through tortures we may expire . . .'

Derek quietly intervened to say that we had run out of time. However, he agreed that monastic orders enabled many medieval women to escape family responsibilities, gain an education, and, in some cases, exert considerable influence. What else had monasticism contributed to medieval society?

Melinda grudgingly conceded that monasteries had done a great service for future generations by preserving and copying manuscripts of the Bible.

'Not just the Bible,' said Wade firmly. 'For centuries monasteries were the main education centres in Europe. Their role in preserving classical literature and developing medieval political, economic and scientific thought is of incalculable importance. And even after the rise of the universities in the twelfth century, monasteries provided the means whereby men and women from lower-class backgrounds could gain an education, and, in the case of men, sometimes rise to prominent positions in the Church. They also witnessed to different values than those which usually prevailed in society.'

'What about helping the poor?' suggested Kirsty. 'And didn't they also give food and beds to travellers, sort of like youth hostels or motels?'

'Yes, they did,' agreed Maureen. 'And nunneries were refuges for widows and women whose husbands had left them. But I don't like the way that they were used as dumping grounds for unwanted children, especially girls. An old medieval poem goes:

> Now earth to earth in convent walls,
> To earth in churchyard sod.
> I was not good enough for man,
> And so am given to God.'

Ruth grimaced. 'It was awful the way children were placed in monasteries by their parents or guardians,' she admitted. 'They cannot possibly have *all* had true vocations. And, once monastic vows were taken in the Middle Ages, there was no way that they could be revoked. Monks and nuns were committed to remain in the monastery of their profession until they died. If they escaped, they were excommunicated, and sometimes hunted down by secular authorities and forcibly returned. I have been sorry to see so many men and women leave religious orders in recent years, but I don't think that they should be forced to remain if they discover that they are not suited to religious life, or, for some reason or other, want to leave. It wouldn't be good for them, or for the rest of the community. Sadly, medieval scholars used to talk about "acedia", a disease characterized by sloth, depression and spiritual aridity, which they regarded as a particularly evil and insidious monastic phenomenon.'

Monasticism

Derek short-circuited Frank's and Melinda's attempts to denounce monasticism as unbiblical, and Ruth finished the tutorial by saying that, as we live in a more secular age, it is easy to underestimate the spiritual duties of medieval monasteries. This, however, was probably their most important contribution to society, as far as most medieval people were concerned. The foundation charter of a tenth-century English monastery (quoted in R. W. Southern's *Western Society and the Church in the Middle Ages*) declared:

> The abbot is armed with spiritual weapons and supported by a troop of monks anointed with the dew of heavenly graces. They fight together in the strength of Christ with the sword of the Spirit against the aery wiles of the devil. They defend the king and the clergy of the realm from the onslaughts of their invisible enemies . . .

Mention of spiritual warfare greatly interested Frank. Everyone else suddenly remembered that they had to rush off somewhere, leaving me trying to look interested in Frank's account of demonic activity in suburbia, while desperately trying to think up an excuse for going too. Just about to successfully escape when Frank started talking about Jason. He has invited him to his Prayer, Praise and Holy Power rally next Sunday night, and claimed his soul for Jesus. Can't somehow share his confidence and enthusiasm.

WEEK·SIX

The papacy

At the time when we were due to start there was no sign of Frank, who was supposed to lead this tutorial. Derek waited anxiously. Eventually the secretary of the Theology Department appeared. Frank had faxed in his tutorial paper and his apologies (he was in the middle of a particularly difficult exorcism and couldn't get away).

Derek began to read Frank's paper aloud. There was something about Revelation, Babylon and Rome.

'Er . . . I think it might be best if we all just pool our ideas,' Derek concluded hastily. 'What were you able to find out about the papacy in the ninth and . . . er . . . tenth centuries?'

'The popes all seem to have come from aristocratic Roman families,' replied Melinda distastefully. 'They were frequently lax, immoral, and involved in Roman politics, which was even more turbulent and sordid in the Dark Ages than it is now.'

'The Pope was chosen by whichever family happened to be dominant at the time,' added Jason eagerly, 'and there were lots of feuds. When Pope Formosus died in 896 his successor, from another family, had his body dug up, stuck on a throne and judged by a tribunal. I don't know what he was supposed to have done, but he was found guilty, stripped of all his pope-clothes and chucked into the River Tiber. A lot of other popes were deposed while still alive, or bumped off. John XII, who became pope when he was eighteen years old, was rumoured to have turned the Lateran palace into a brothel, and he supposedly died in 964 of "amorous excess" while making love. What a way to go!'

'And the city of Rome was frightfully decayed,' sighed Christobel. 'The population had declined dramatically since the days when it was the greatest city in the Roman Empire. There were ruins everywhere. It must have been awfully squalid and depressing.'

'The Pope rarely had the power to control the city effectively, let alone extend his influence elsewhere,' declared Wade. 'His ability to communicate with the wider Church was severely limited.'

'There were no mobile phones, fax machines, satellites, aeroplanes – not even posties on push-bikes,' interjected Jason in a pitying tone.

'But Rome was still revered by Christians because it contained the physical remains of St Peter and St Paul,' said Ruth, 'and pilgrimages to the city remained very popular. King Canute of England went there in 1027 and wrote . . .' Ruth thumbed through R. W. Southern's *The Making of the Middle Ages.* 'Here we are, page 132:

God has granted me in my lifetime the boon of visiting the blessed Apostles Peter and Paul and every sanctuary within and without the city of Rome that I could hear of, to venerate and adore them in their very presence . . . And I sought this blessing because I heard from wise men that St Peter the Apostle has received from the Lord a great power of binding and loosing, and bears the keys of the kingdom of heaven; and therefore I deemed it useful in no ordinary degree to seek his patronage before God.'

'Superstitious nonsense!' said Melinda disdainfully.

'Furthermore,' continued Ruth in a more determined voice, 'the papal administration never quite broke down, whatever the shortcomings of individual popes, and in countries beyond Rome the Pope remained an exalted figure, albeit an almost legendary one.'

'The tenth century witnessed the emergence of a new dynasty of German kings out of the anarchy that followed the disintegration of the Carolingian Empire,' lectured Wade. 'Otto the Great lived from 912 to 973 and became the most powerful ruler in Europe. Part of the reason for his success was the fact that he controlled the German church, and its not inconsiderable wealth and power. We should remember that church leaders at the time sometimes had their own armies and courts, and the rights to exact tolls, establish markets and mint money. In return for privileges like these, the king expected that he would have the major say in the appointment of new church leaders, and receive such things as hospitality on his travels, troops for his army and counsel at his courts. He naturally only appointed bishops and abbots who were his loyal supporters, and who would be prepared to serve as government officials and balance the power of the hereditary secular nobility. Anyway, in 962 Otto "rescued" the Pope from the Italian aristocracy and was crowned emperor in return.'

'The Pope was clearly trying to recreate a Western empire to bolster his position against the Byzantine Empire at a time when Byzantine forces were advancing through southern Italy,' stated Melinda.

'Well, if he was,' replied Wade, 'he only exchanged one possible overlord for another. Otto took firm control of the papacy and deposed and appointed popes, just as he did bishops and abbots in Germany.'

'But he was really quite religious,' remarked Christobel, 'and he was married to a wonderfully intelligent and devout wife, Adelaide. She encouraged learning and the fine arts throughout the empire. Actually, I think that what is known as the Ottonian Renaissance really should be called the Adelaidian Renaissance. Adelaide was also a great supporter of monasteries and missions to the pagans, and, after the deaths of her husband and son, she ruled the empire very capably until her grandson came of age.'

Ruth pointed out that the German monarchy had strong connections with Cluny, and actively supported the Cluniac reform movement which we briefly considered last week. Adelaide's spiritual director was Odilo, who became one of the greatest abbots of Cluny, and Henry III, emperor from 1039 to 1056, was a friend of Abbot Hugh. He appointed reforming priests to bishoprics in the empire and reforming German bishops to the papacy. Three of the four popes he appointed died before they could do much, but one, Leo IX, lasted from 1049 to 1054. Leo was not a member of the Roman aristocracy, so he could rise above Roman feuds, and he surrounded himself with men of intelligence and integrity who were dedicated to reforming the Church.

Maureen, who had been sitting quietly throughout the tutorial, now seized the opportunity to make a contribution. 'Leo didn't hang around Rome being corrupt and immoral like other popes. He rushed all over Europe, holding councils with local bishops and priests, and those who tried to oppose him were miraculously tongue-tied or dropped down dead. When he couldn't go somewhere personally, he sent off papal leggings . . .'

'I think you mean *legates*,' corrected Ruth with a smile.

'What abuses did Leo and his . . . er . . . fellow reformers particularly want to correct?' enquired Derek. 'Could you find out anything about that, Michael?'

I managed to bleat out: 'Simony (which I think means buying and selling gifts of the spirit, including church offices), and priests getting married or keeping concubines.'

Christobel muttered something about warped sexuality and the influence of paganism.

'Perhaps more directly the influence of monasticism,' murmured Derek. 'Opposition to married priests was . . . er . . . partly based on the notion of ritual purity and partly on practical considerations. Married priests were supposedly squandering church money on their families and passing their jobs onto their sons.'

'From what I have read the eleventh-century reform move-ment has been overrated,' said Wade. 'Various attempts had been made to regulate priests' relationship with women in previous centuries. It is hard to say whether those in the eleventh century were more successful.'

'But it is quite certain that they were not unopposed,' insisted Christobel. 'Bishops who tried to enforce celibacy risked getting lynched or stoned, not just by married priests but by their enraged wives!'

Maureen whole-heartedly approved of this rather drastic response.

'Simony was also condemned throughout the history of the Church,' commented Ruth, 'but it may have been an increasing problem in the eleventh century because of the spread of the money economy. It must have been a very diffi-cult issue because, traditionally, presents were given by newly appointed priests, abbots or bishops to the person who conferred their church, monastery or bishopric. Did this count as simony or courtesy? If it was simony, were their ordi-nations or consecrations invalid?'

'And linked to the controversy over simony was the debate over whether laymen should have the right to confer churches, monasteries or bishoprics at all,' said Wade. 'It certainly seems strange to us that laymen could own churches, collect tithes and appoint clergy, but again this was not a clear-cut issue at the time. Devout laymen (like Henry III) seem to have carried out their responsibilities quite conscientiously, while clerical owners were not necessarily manifestly superior. In fact, bishops and monasteries were notorious for ripping off parish churches under their control – taking their income and paying the incumbent cleric a mere pittance.'

'It appears quite clear to me', announced Melinda, 'that the so-called papal reformers were far more interested in increasing papal prestige and authority than promoting the moral rejuvenation of the clergy and better instruction and pastoral care for the laity. This precipitated a split between the East and the West. In 1054 the papal legate, Cardinal Humbert, excommunicated the Patriarch of Constantinople, who reciprocated by excommunicating the Pope. I am sorry to say that both sides degenerated to quite unChristian rudeness and abuse.'

Derek pointed out that a long series of incidents and developments had gradually caused the Greek and Latin churches to grow further apart. Apart from the obvious language difference, they developed different liturgical forms and different attitudes to married clergy. Another bone of contention was the Latin addition of the 'Filioque' clause to the Nicene Creed in the early eleventh century: 'And I believe in the Holy Spirit, the Lord and giver of life, who proceedeth from the Father *and the Son* . . .' In short, the year 1054 is no longer regarded as the definite beginning of the schism between the two great branches of Christianity.

'Henry III died in 1056,' said Wade, ignoring this

digression. 'His heir was a child too young to assume control of the empire, and the papal reformers took advantage of this and elected Nicholas II pope in 1059 without the new emperor's consent. Nicholas promptly presided over a synod which decreed that henceforth popes could only be elected by cardinals, not appointed by secular rulers. This has continued to be the case to the present day. The decree of 1059 naturally increased the importance of cardinals, and so it could be said to represent the beginning of the Roman curia, the corporate organization of the Roman Church, although the papal administration remained very small and limited until well into the following century.'

'After the synod of 1059 Nicholas entered into an alliance with Robert Guiscard, the leader of the Normans,' remarked Jason. 'The Normans, the most feared warriors in Europe, were successfully and violently invading southern Italy. In fact, in 1053 Leo IX led an army against them but he was defeated and held captive for almost a year. Nicholas reversed Leo's policy and recognized the Normans' right to occupy their conquered lands, and, in return, Robert promised to come to the papacy's defence whenever needed, and to ensure that future elections of popes proceeded smoothly.'

'I think that Nicholas's synod also decreed that no priest was to be appointed to a church by a lay person,' added Ruth, 'and it ordered people to stay away from masses said by priests who were living with women.'

'Oh,' said Maureen, 'a lay strike! One of my friends was only saying the other day that she wasn't going to go to church again until the minister stopped making the congregation sing the Lord's Prayer. She thinks it should be said quietly and reverently. I personally don't mind singing it, but I wish the Sunday School teachers wouldn't keep encouraging the youth group to bring its drum kit and guitars. It wouldn't be so bad if the kids could actually play them . . .'

Melinda expressed her opinion that the Lord's Prayer should be solemnly recited, while Christobel insisted that it was vitally important that the youth be included in the service.

'Er . . . one of the most active participants in the papal reform movement in the eleventh century was a Cluniac monk called Hildebrand,' intervened Derek. 'He was elected pope in . . . er . . . 1073 and took the name Gregory VII. He became so famous that the whole reform movement is sometimes called the Gregorian Reform. What could you find out about him?'

'He was clearly an arrogant, worldly man who was driven by an ambition to dominate Europe,' declared Melinda. 'He made the most outrageous claims on behalf of the papacy. Southern lists some of them in *Western Society and the Church in the Middle Ages* (p. 102):

> The pope can be judged by no one;
> the Roman Church has never erred and never will err till the end of time;
> the Roman Church was founded by Christ alone;
> the pope alone can depose and restore bishops;
> he alone can make new laws, set up new bishoprics, and divide old ones;
> he alone can translate bishops;
> he alone can call general councils and authorize canon law;
> he alone can revise his own judgements;
> he alone can use the imperial insignia;
> he can depose emperors;
> he can absolve subjects from their allegiance;
> all princes should kiss his feet;
> his legates, even though in inferior orders, have precedence over all bishops;
> an appeal to the papal court inhibits judgement by all inferior courts;

a duly ordained pope is undoubtedly made a saint by the
     merits of St Peter.'

'They are extravagant claims,' conceded Ruth, 'but I don't
think that they were so much a blueprint for papal absolutism
as a response to an emergency. Gregory did genuinely strive
for the moral reform of the Church; he especially wanted to
suppress simony and clerical marriage. However, unless he
could free the Church from secular control, and, in particular, the papacy from the whims of the Italian aristocracy and
the German monarchy, he didn't stand much chance of
succeeding. Henry IV was a less devout supporter of Church
reform than his father had been.'

'The trouble was, Henry IV was confronted by rebellious
nobles and he could not afford to lose control of the appointment of bishops,' added Wade.

'He was not prepared to . . . er . . . forsake the right to
"invest" new bishops with their ring and staff, the . . . er . . .
symbols of episcopal office, and hence his conflict with
Gregory is often called the Investiture Controversy,' said
Derek conscientiously, 'although that was not the only issue.'

'In 1075, or thereabouts, a dispute arose over the appointment of the Archbishop of Milan,' said Maureen, checking
her notes. 'Henry wanted to give the ring-and-staff thing
to one person, and Gregory to another. Eventually Greg
wrote to Henry, rebuked him for interfering and reminded
him of what had happened to Saul. Henry then called a
council of not-so-keen-to-be-reformed-by-the-Pope bishops
and Greg was denounced as that "monk Hildebrand"
who had unlawfully become pope. As soon as he heard
about this Greg excommunicated Henry and declared that
Henry's subjects no longer had to obey him. Heaps of
them were real glad about this, and, faced with a massive

rebellion, Henry had to crawl to Greg and beg for forgiveness.'

'It was the middle of winter, and, after a horrendous journey across the Alps, poor Henry had to wait outside the castle where the Pope was staying at Canossa for three days,' said Christobel in a sympathetic tone. 'He was left barefoot in the snow, dressed in humble clothes, crying for forgiveness. It must have been terribly humiliating for him.'

'If you ask me, it was all a big act,' said Maureen caustically. 'As a Christian, Greg had to forgive him, but as soon as Henry got back to Germany and resumed control of his kingdom he declared Greg deposed and got the German bishops to elect a new pope, Clement III. Greg tried to excommunicate him again, but this time Henry came to Rome with his army, kicked Greg out and got Clem to crown him emperor. Robert Guiscard and the Normans intervened on behalf of Greg, but they did so much damage in Rome that Greg had to retreat with them to southern Italy to escape the anger of the Roman citizens. He ended up dying in exile in 1085.'

'So the papal claims which Melinda read out a little while ago were a big joke,' said Wade, crossing his arms. 'Gregory alienated many bishops, archbishops and nobles with his high-handed behaviour and they simply resisted or ignored him. At one stage he tried to bring Robert Guisard to heel by excommunicating him, but Robert lived for more than six years without appearing to be unduly troubled by the threat of eternal damnation. In England, William the Conqueror took firm control of the church (with the help of Archbishop Lanfranc of Canterbury) and he refused to allow English bishops to visit Rome or papal legates to enter the kingdom.'

Melinda nodded. 'To that I would like to add that the Pope's conflict with the German empire should not be portrayed as a conflict of reformers versus non-reformers,' she said. 'I read that Henry's personal copy of the Psalter was practically worn out with use, and Clement III appears to have been a capable pope and moderate reformer, by no means a mere puppet of the emperor. Furthermore, Maureen, you omitted to say that Gregory actually declared Henry excommunicated in 1080 *before* Henry declared Gregory deposed and marched on Rome. Overall, it is quite clear that the dispute was basically over two very different concepts of rulership: papal primacy versus sacral kingship.'

'It must have been very difficult for people caught in the middle,' said Christobel, seizing the moment to get a word in, 'people like Matilda, Countess of Tuscany. She owned enormous estates in northern and central Italy and virtually controlled several of the major roads between Germany and Rome. She was actually a great friend and advisor of Gregory VII, and at Canossa (which, incidentally, was one of her castles), she encouraged him to give Henry absolution. Then, after Gregory's death, she supported his successor Urban II rather than Clement III, which probably contributed greatly to Urban establishing himself as the legitimate pope. And she was also a great patron of learning, had a wonderful library and supported lots of scholars.'

'Urban II had been a close associate of Gregory VII and supported his reforming legislation but he was perhaps a bit more . . . er . . . diplomatic,' said Derek, glancing at his watch. 'The election of another Cluniac monk, Paschal II, in 1099 and the death of Clement III in . . . er . . . 1100 virtually ended the schism. Paschal and following popes did not insist on the removal of bishops and clergy ordained in obedience to Clement, and they didn't push the attack on simony and concubinage. Paschal did, however, take a firm stand on the issue of lay investiture, and disputes with Henry IV's son Henry V continued into the eleventh century until a compromise was agreed on. According to the concordat of Worms (1122) the emperor ... er ... surrendered his claim to nominate bishops and invest them with ring and staff, while the Pope agreed that the election of bishops in Germany might take place in the emperor's presence, that he could settle disputed elections, and that he could bestow on bishops the "regalia" (temporal jurisdiction of cities, duchies, rights to markets, tolls, minting coins, etc.) which were symbolized by the sceptre.'

'Which, in practice, meant that the emperor retained great influence,' commented Wade.

'Really, the problem of Church and State, and which has authority over what, has never gone away,' said Maureen reflectively. 'Take the Church of England for instance. I don't mind Queen Elizabeth II being its head or governor or whatever the monarch is supposed to be, but I'm not so sure about Prince Charles, and what would happen if Prince William turned out to be an atheist? If there were royal elections, I'd vote Anne for queen.'

'The British monarch doesn't actually have much say in the running of the Anglican Church,' responded Wade, 'but should the Prime Minister and British Parliament continue to play a significant role in such matters as the appointment of bishops, changes to the prayer book, and issues like the ordination of women?'

'I must admit that I find the organization of the Church of England vastly preferable to that of the Roman Catholic Church,' said Melinda. 'I am afraid that the current aims of the Vatican are not too far removed from those of the Gregorian age, especially now that the Cold War is over and the Pope is trying to extend his influence in eastern Europe. The Church hierarchy seems to conveniently forget that Jesus, when he was tempted by the devil, rejected the offer of power ...'

At this point Ruth abruptly announced that she was sorry but she had to leave to attend a meeting. The rest of us got ready to go, too.

'Isn't Malignant Melinda a pain?' said Jason to me as we drifted towards the refectory. 'But at least we were spared Fundamentalist Frank. If you want some really good advice, NEVER go to anything he invites you to. I let curiosity get the better of me and did I regret it!'

'You went to the Prayer, Praise and Holy Power rally?' I enquired conversationally.

'There was well over an HOUR of singing', replied Jason in loathing. 'All those mushy "I love you so-o-o, Lord" choruses made me want to throw up. And we had to sing them over and over and over again till I was almost bored out of my mind. THEN the guy who was leading the "worship" said: 'Won't it be fantastic when we can go on praising Jesus like this FOR ETERNITY?" That might be his idea of heaven, but it's my idea of hell! Fading into nothingness on your deathbed is INFINITELY preferable. The only break we got was when we were told to turn around and give the person behind us a hug. Fortunately, the person in front of me took one look at my face and decided to make do with a handshake.'

I asked if there had been a speaker. 'Oh, God, yes,' said Jason. 'I thought that he was going to go on for ever, too. He claimed that he hadn't prepared his message, he was just going to let the Holy Spirit speak through him. Well, if that was the Holy Spirit, he/she/it is the most disorganized waffler I have ever had the misfortune to come across. The only point that I could really catch was that the Pope is the Antichrist. I remember that because the "Holy Spirit" produced pictures of Catholics bowing down before the Pope in St Peter's Square as proof. There was a lot more talk about the Book of Revelation, 666, the international money market and Armageddon happening in Iraq, but I was having trouble staying awake by then so the finer details passed me by.'

'Did any miracles take place?'

Jason snorted contemptuously. 'When the speaker finally finished running down the Pope, and prophesying gloom, doom and Judgement Day, he said that the Holy Spirit was telling him that someone in the audience had a headache. I ask you, after all that singing and verbal diarrhoea, what else could he expect? I was fast developing a raging migraine! Of course, a couple of people did get up, so he yelled some orders to God on their behalf. Then he started exhorting anyone who wasn't "saved" to give his/her heart to Jesus. Apparently to do that you had to go down to the front. There was no way on earth that I was going to walk out there, even if I had wanted to "give my heart to Jesus". But the speaker went on and on, exhorting people to go down to the front. Eventually he reckoned that the Holy Spirit was telling him that he wanted someone whose name began with "J" to make a commitment. Well, either Frank had told him that I might be there, or he figured that in a crowd of people there'd be quite a few "Js". In any case, I got up all right – and bolted to the door. A couple rushed up to me crying: "Have you ever spoken in tongues?" but I pushed past them, ran to my motorbike and roared off. I copped a speeding ticket a kilometre down the road, but it was worth it to get away. If that is Christianity, you can count me out!'

Week·Seven

The crusades

Kirsty started her tutorial by revealing that Mohammed died in AD 632. She supposed that we all knew who Mohammed was. He worshipped Allah, more or less the same God as the Jews and the Christians, but he believed that Allah had sent him as a prophet. Jesus had also been a prophet, not Allah's only son. Mohammed's thoughts are recorded in the Koran. The religious movement he developed is known as Islam, which means submission, and his followers are called Muslims (those who submit).

'Jesus warned us that false prophets would arise and try to deceive the elect,' interjected Frank. Melinda agreed.

Kirsty tried to highlight the success of Islam. Mohammed united the nomadic tribes of Arabia with his new religion, and after his death his followers captured Damascus (635), Jerusalem (638), Alexandria (642), Persia (651) and Carthage (698). By 717 the Islamic empire stretched from the Pyrenees to India.

'Yeah, well, their success was due to the fact that Mohammed encouraged aggression,' declared Frank. 'Evangelism was by the sword. It's a basic belief of Islam that if you die in a holy war you go straight to paradise where you will live in luxury surrounded by lots of beautiful women.'

'Very immoral,' said Melinda, 'but, unfortunately, likely to appeal to certain types of people.'

'Muslims succeeded in conquering such vast territory because the Byzantine and Persian Empires were exhausted after a series of wars,' responded Wade with an exasperated sigh. 'Furthermore, Christians in Egypt and Syria were disillusioned with the imperial government's heavy taxation, corruption and repression of supposedly heretical movements. It was easier to submit to the relatively tolerant Islamic forces than fight against them.'

'And Islamic culture was frightfully impressive in the Middle Ages,' enthused Christobel. 'Scholarship, in particular, far exceeded that in western Europe. Astronomy, mathematics, physics, chemistry, medicine, philosophy, history, law, literature, poetry: you name it, they did it *brilliantly*. Islamic surgeons even used anaesthetics, at a time when patients in the West were lucky if they got a bump on the head! And there were fabulous luxury goods in the East: silks, perfumes, spices, jewels . . .'

Melinda didn't look too impressed, and Frank muttered something about luxury and decadence.

'Moving on to the First Crusade,' began Kirsty, frantically thumbing through her notes, 'Pope Urban II is usually said to have started it by preaching a sermon at Clermont in France in 1095. What do you think could have . . . um . . . motivated him?'

'All the atrocities committed by the Muslims,' said Frank confidently. 'Urban told the knights at Clermont:

From the confines of Jerusalem and the city of Constantinople a horrible tale has gone forth . . . that a race from the kingdom of the Persians, an accursed race, a race utterly alienated from God . . . has invaded the lands of those Christians and has depopulated them by the sword, pillage and fire; it has led away a part of the captives into its own country, and a part it has destroyed by cruel tortures; it has either entirely destroyed the churches of God or appropriated them for the rites of its own religion . . . When they wish to torture people by a base death, they perforate their navels, and dragging forth the extremity of the intestines, bind it to a stake; then with flogging they lead the victim around until the viscera having gushed forth the victim falls prostrate on the ground . . . What shall I say of the abominable rape of the women? To speak of it is worse than to be silent . . .'

'There are several different versions of the speech extant and no one is sure which is the most accurate,' declared Wade. 'Frank has just read from Robert the Monk's account which is in E. Peter's *The First Crusade: The Chronicle of Fulcher of Chartres and Other Source Materials*. It was written a generation after the event. The atrocity stories were clearly greatly exaggerated. Muslims were by and large tolerant towards Christians and Jews, whom they recognized as ultimately worshipping Allah, albeit in a corrupt way. Christians were allowed to practise their religion as long as they paid a special tax, didn't attempt to win converts, and so on. Christian pilgrims from western Europe were also permitted to visit the Holy Land because tourism was then, as now, a valuable source of revenue.'

'But in the eleventh century the Turks arrived on the scene, and they were more fanatical and hard to get on with than other Muslims,' objected Maureen. 'My eldest daughter went on a bus tour of Europe a few years ago, and she didn't like Turkey at all. When they got to the border . . .'

'The Turks had wrested control of Asia Minor from the Byzantine Empire and were within striking distance of Constantinople,' said Wade, cutting Maureen off.

'Accordingly, in 1095 the emperor appealed to Pope Urban II for help.'

'But Urban really called the First Crusade to increase his own power and prestige,' claimed Melinda. 'Gregory VII had wanted to lead a crusade, too, but he spent his time fighting Henry IV instead. As a result of Gregory's humiliating defeat in the Investiture Controversy, and the ongoing schism with Clement III, Urban was determined to enlist as many fighting men as possible in his service. He must have hoped that they would bolster his position in western Europe, and force the Greek Church to acknowledge the primacy of Rome in return for military aid.'

'I'm afraid that war was a reality of life in medieval Europe,' mused Ruth. 'The warrior ethos must have been strongly entrenched in the culture of the Germanic tribes which took over the western part of the Roman Empire in the early Middle Ages, and the Viking, Muslim and Magyar invasions of the ninth century would have done nothing to discourage it.'

'After the decline of the central power of the Carolingian state in the ninth century, the problem was not so much large-scale warfare,' contributed Derek, 'but . . . er . . . lots of disputes and feuds. Groups of knights based at different castles would engage in skirmishes which could be very damaging at a local level. Er . . . fields could be ravaged, harvests destroyed, herds driven off and houses burnt. So how did the Church . . . er . . . respond?'

'What the Church could not prevent, it at least tried to limit,' answered Ruth. 'I think that it was in the tenth century that the Peace of God movement arose, which was later extended to the Truce of God. Knights were exhorted to protect the weak, the defenceless and the Church, and to abstain from fighting on certain days. The abbots of Cluny were heavily involved in promoting the Peace and Truce of God, and Abbot Odo wrote a biography of St Gerald of Aurillac. He was a knight who was pious, meek and humble, and always turned the other cheek, except when defending the Church and the poor: hopefully, a good role model for other knights.'

'Of course, the Church built on Augustine's doctrine of a just war,' asserted Wade. 'Christians could participate in a war if it had been declared by a legitimate authority for a just cause. The Church also fostered the sacramental mystique of knighthood: if conducted properly, it was a noble vocation; clergy could pray for individual knights and bless their swords; military expeditions (such as the Norman conquest of England in 1066) could be blessed by the papacy; knights in the service of the Pope could be called "knights of St Peter" or "knights of Christ" . . .'

'Which was a frightful betrayal of the Church's pacifist origins!' burst out Christobel. '"Knights of Christ" indeed! I shudder to think what the Prince of Peace must have thought. Pilgrimages initially weren't so bad,' she conceded. 'I know how inspiring it can be to visit places where famous poets and artists have lived and just soak up the atmosphere. Sometimes, in a mystical way, I feel that I can commune with their spirits. Well, medieval people simply loved visiting saints' shrines, and, above all, the Holy Land, because it was simply littered with saints' relics and holy sites. But travelling wasn't easy in those days, and the Church started imposing obligations to go on pilgrimages as penances for sin. It was really an awfully good idea, because sinners either had a deep and meaningful spiritual experience at the holy place or they arrived home too broke and exhausted to sin any more. Anyway, in 1095 Urban II came up with the absolutely appalling idea of sending people on *armed pilgrimages*. Instead of being a sin, it would be a Good Thing to visit the

Holy Land and kill a few Muslims. All your sins would be forgiven, and you'd get instant access to heaven.'

'There has been a lot of debate over what exactly Urban offered the knights at Clermont,' said Derek doubtfully. 'The doctrines of purgatory, remission of temporal penalties, remission of penance, and the treasury of merits were . . . er . . . far from clearly formulated in the eleventh century. However, rightly or wrongly, word did seem to get around that the Pope had guaranteed remission of sins.'

'Urban cynically manipulated his audience,' stated Melinda, 'until those present were roused to cry: "It is the will of God! It is the will of God!" And, although Urban targeted experienced knights, itinerant evangelists spread the message around the countryside, with emotional tirades at mass meetings. Miracles were even thought to occur, and a lot of emphasis was placed on the supposedly imminent Second Coming. This had a very harmful affect on ignorant people. Such fanaticism and folly! One is forcibly reminded of aspects of the twentieth-century Pentecostal movement.'

'At least medieval people had great faith,' retorted Frank, indignant at the slur on Pentecostalism. 'They were prepared to leave home and family for the sake of Christ.'

'That certainly appears to be true from a superficial glance at the crusades,' intervened Wade. 'However, the real causes of the crusading movement were not religious but economic and social. There was increasing prosperity in western Europe after AD1000. Life became less precarious, food production rose, and the size of families increased. The growing popularity of the practice of primogeniture meant that lots of younger sons were forced to seek their fame and fortune away from the family home. According to Robert the Monk, Urban II appealed to young knights' desire for wealth and adventure at Clermont:

This land which you inhabit, shut in on all sides by the seas and surrounded by the mountain peaks, is too narrow for your large population; nor does it abound in wealth; and it furnishes scarcely food enough for its cultivators. Hence it is that you murder one another, that you wage war, and that frequently you perish by mutual wounds. Let therefore hatred depart from among you . . . Enter upon the road to the Holy Sepulchre [in Jerusalem]; wrest that land from the wicked race, and subject it to yourselves. That land which as the Scripture says "floweth with milk and honey" . . .

'The idea of emigrating would also have appealed to the thousands of poor men and women who answered the call of itinerant evangelists because they had just experienced a couple of seasons of drought and poor harvests.'

'Nevertheless, I don't think that we should underestimate medieval people's piety,' argued Ruth gently. 'Crusaders, rich or poor, faced great hardships and great expenses. For some at least, the crusades seem to have provided a "way of the cross" that was an alternative to entering a monastery. Whereas monks and nuns made an "interior" journey to Jerusalem and engaged in spiritual warfare, crusaders did so more literally. In a semi-monastic way they also withdrew from the world they had known (leaving behind home and family), took vows (albeit temporary), endured poverty and hardship (and perhaps celibacy), and shared in regular public devotions.'

Derek agreed that some historians have linked the crusades to the 'monasticization of the Church' fostered by the eleventh-century papal reform movement.

'Whatever their motives for going, Urban hadn't wanted an unruly rabble to set off for Palestine,' observed Maureen. 'He only wanted experienced knights, and so he must have been real cross with Peter the Hermit and others who went around preaching the crusade to anyone who'd listen.'

'The rabble didn't swarm into Rome, though,' pointed out Jason. 'It's the people who lived on the route to Constantinople that I feel sorry for. The so-called "People's Crusade" had precious little money or supplies, so it pillaged and fought its way through eastern Europe. The official papal-sponsored crusade was little better behaved.'

'And there was an awful lot of xenophobia and anti-Semitism,' said Christobel with a shudder. 'The crusaders massacred hundreds of Jews, in a terribly misguided attempt to avenge Christ's death.'

'The wealth of the Jews was probably more significant than their religion,' interjected Wade cynically.

'Anyway,' concluded Jason, 'the crusaders, who survived exhaustion, starvation, fighting, flooded rivers, and goodness know how many other hardships, eventually reached Constantinople – to the horror of the emperor. He shipped them across the Bosporus to Asia Minor as quickly as possible. Untrained peasants were promptly slaughtered by the Turks. The official crusade had better success, due to good luck more than anything else. The Muslims were so busy fighting among themselves that the crusaders were able to capture Jerusalem in 1099.'

'The knights must have made an awesome sight,' exclaimed Kirsty, 'charging towards the enemy on horseback, with their armour glistening in the sun, crosses sewn onto their cloaks ...'

'Actually, I read somewhere that the average height of medieval men was quite a bit smaller than today,' commented Maureen. 'And they hardly ever washed. Just image the stink by the time they got to Palestine! I don't fancy dirty, smelly, malnourished knights at all.'

Kirsty looked a bit deflated.

'Winter weather made armour rust, and the summer heat

proved so unbearable that many knights chucked it away,' added Jason eagerly. 'Exhaustion, thirst and famine took a heavy toll, as well. Knights even bled their horses to drink their blood, and many killed and ate them.' Kirsty began to look pale, but there was worse to come. 'The rabble had to make do with eating dogs and rats, and grain teased from animal dung. During the attack on Antioch in 1098–9 crusaders were so starving that, according to one chronicle, they cut pieces of flesh from the buttocks of dead Muslims and cooked and ate them, "savagely devouring the flesh while it was insufficiently roasted". And diseases were rife, especially dysentery. King Louis of France had to relieve himself so often on the Sixth Crusade that he cut the bottoms out of his pants to save time.

'As for the actual fighting, when the Christian crusaders entered Jerusalem in 1099, they slaughtered *all* Muslim and Jewish men, women and children. They waded to the Church of the Holy Sepulchre, ankle-deep in blood, to praise God for their victory. A chronicler wrote: "It was a just and splendid judgement of God that this place should be filled with the blood of the unbelievers . . . The city was filled with corpses and blood." ' Felt slightly sick.

After an uncomfortable silence, Wade spoke in a quieter voice than usual. 'All wars are horrific, but I think that wars fought with religious overtones are the worst of all. Enemies that are thought to be eternally damned become sub-human, and atrocities can be justified as the will of God.'

'Like King Richard ("the Lionheart") of England's capture of Acre in 1191,' suggested Jason. 'When the garrison surrendered, Richard had all the Muslims bound and killed. According to a Christian writer quoted in Ronald Finucane's *Soldiers of the Faith: Crusaders and Muslims at War*:

Two thousand seven hundred, all
In chains, were led outside the wall,
Where they were slaughtered every one ...
For this be the Creator blessed!

'A Muslim put it this way: "They brought out the Muslim prisoners, whom God had pre-ordained to martyrdom that day, to the number of more than three thousand, all tied together with ropes. The Franks rushed upon them all at once and slaughtered them in cold blood . . ." Then, a hundred years later: "God permitted the Muslims to reconquer [Acre] . . . the Sultan gave his word to the Franks and then had them slaughtered as the Franks had done to the Muslims. Thus Almighty God was revenged on their descendants." '

'That's what's so awful about war!' cried Christobel. 'One violent act provokes another, and so on, and so on. King Richard's Muslim adversary, Saladin, was really quite noble and chivalrous (high-ranking Christian prisoners of war were even invited to his banquets), but after the massacre at Acre he retaliated by killing his prisoners. Retaliation . . . counter-retaliation . . . a dreadful spiral . . .'

'What do you think the crusades achieved, apart from obviously worsening Christian–Muslim relations?' asked Derek.

'They didn't do much for relations between Eastern Orthodox and Western Catholic Christians, either,' replied Maureen. 'The Fourth Crusade ended up attacking and conquering Constantinople! I read somewhere that the crusades weakened the Byzantine Empire so much that it was vulnerable to the Turks, who finally seized Constantinople sometime in the fifteenth century, I forget when.'

'1453,' murmured Derek. 'And . . . er . . . scholars now

believe that it was the crusades, rather than the eleventh-century papal reform movement, which made the break between Rome and Constantinople irreversible.'

'They also didn't do much for the unity of western Europe,' said Jason contemptuously. 'Disputes were continually breaking out between the different nationalities involved, especially the French, German and English forces. The Pope might have started the crusading movement, but once it got underway the Church had precious little control over it!'

'Some clergy actually took part in the fighting,' said Christobel in horrified tones. 'And military orders arose, which were an absolutely abhorrent form of monasticism.'

'The knight-monks (the Templars, Hospitallers, and Teutonic knights) were also frequently at loggerheads,' added Wade with a rueful smile. 'Likewise, the "Christian" states founded in the Middle East after the "successful" First Crusade were racked by family feuds and jealousy. Further crusades tried to defend them, but they were gradually reconquered by the Muslims. Jerusalem fell in 1187, and the last crusading stronghold, Acre, in 1291. As Runciman says at the end of his three-volume history of the crusades: "Seen in the perspective of history the whole crusading movement was a vast fiasco." '

'Didn't the crusades sort of encourage trade around the Mediterranean, and spread Islamic culture to western Europe?' ventured Kirsty.

'That is a myth,' retorted Wade crushingly. 'Long before the crusades, ships were sailing between Italy, Byzantium, Egypt and Syria. Many Christian pilgrims came into contact with Islamic culture in Palestine, and there was considerable interaction between Christians and Muslims in Spain and southern Italy. The ignorant, fanatical crusaders had little time for Islamic culture, and little impact on it.'

'But the crusades did inspire a lot of chronicles and poems,' insisted Kirsty, in one last desperate attempt to show how well she had prepared for this tutorial.

'Like the poem about the knight attacked by a Muslim while squatting to relieve himself,' interjected Jason nonchalantly. ' "It was most cowardly and base/To take a knight thus unaware/While occupied in such affair . . ." I found that in Finucane's book. He also quotes a Muslim chronicler's account of the Christian prostitutes who followed the crusaders:

> They dedicated as a holy offering what they kept between their thighs; they were openly licentious . . . brought their silver anklets up to touch their golden ear-rings, and were willingly spread out on the carpet of amorous sport . . . They were the places where tent-pegs were driven in, they invited swords to enter their sheaths . . . welcomed birds into the nest of their thighs, caught in their net the horns of butting rams . . .'

'Do you have to dredge up the most disgusting stories that you can possibly find?' snapped Melinda, seething with indignation and exasperation.

'Alas, some women were forced into prostitution,' admitted Christobel regretfully. 'But, while I absolutely abhor war, there were also women brave enough to take part in the actual fighting, while others nobly tended the sick and the wounded. Countless others "kept the home fires burning". Sadly, we have so little information about them because historians have nearly always focused on men. Overall, however, I'm afraid that the crusades did tend to foster sexist male values . . .'

'One of the worst features of the crusades for me was the anti-Semitism,' admitted Ruth. 'Even an Abbot of Cluny wrote: "What is the good of going to the end of the world at great loss of men and money to fight the Saracens, when we permit among us other infidels who are a thousand times more guilty towards Christ than the Mohammedans?"'

'They should have tried to convert them, not kill them,' conceded Frank, 'but you have to admire the faith of the men of the Middle Ages. Painter says in A *History of the Middle Ages 284–1500* that:

The Crusades . . . are at once the chief proof of the tremendous vitality and expansive power of medieval civilization and the most concrete illustration of the meaning of the common expression "an Age of Faith". Although some men undoubtedly went crusading in search of fiefs and plunder, because they found their native land too hot for them, or simply from love of adventure, it seems clear that the majority were moved by genuine religious enthusiasm and complete confidence that the crusade was the path to salvation. Innumerable men mortgaged or even sold their lands, left their wives and families, and faced the terrors of a long journey through inhospitable lands or over fearsome seas to serve God against his foes. The general assumption was that a crusader would never return home. Although many did return, usually worn and bankrupt, far more found their graves in distant lands. To all who question the faith of the men of the Middle Ages the Crusades stand as a crushing refutation.'

Christobel crossly remarked that the absence of any reference to women's contribution to the crusades in that quotation proved her previous point. Ruth, however, said that she preferred Runciman's conclusion:

The Crusades were a tragic and destructive episode . . . There was so much courage and so little honour, so much devotion and so little understanding. High ideals were besmirched by cruelty and greed, enterprise and endurance by a blind and narrow self-righteousness; and the Holy War itself was nothing more than a long act of intolerance in the name of God . . .

'And xenophobia, anti-Semitism, religious fanaticism, militarism, ignorance, intolerance and greed did not die out in the Middle Ages,' said Wade soberly. 'In my opinion, the greatest tragedy of the crusades is the fact that the one institution in Western society that could and should have restrained such vile forces, the Church, actually promoted them. Will Christians be more successful as we move into the twenty-first century?'

Considering the number of places in the world that are currently experiencing warfare and violence, this was a depressing note to finish on.

WEEK·EIGHT

The twelfth-century Renaissance

Another one of our general group discussions. Melinda arrived looking tired and cross. She said that she had a sore throat, it had taken her ages to find a parking spot for her car, which had made her late, and she had tripped hurrying up the stairs. All in all, she wished that she had stayed at home.

'Don't we all,' murmured Jason cryptically.

Derek tried to introduce today's topic: the twelfth-century Renaissance.

Melinda immediately took exception to his use of the term 'Renaissance'. 'It was not a true Renaissance because there was no significant rebirth of classical culture,' she croaked. 'It is quite unworthy of comparison with THE Renaissance of the fifteenth century.'

'Historians have argued over the precise meaning of "Renaissance",' responded Derek, 'and whether it is appropriate to use it in the medieval context or not. Could we just put that debate aside for the time being and consider what actually happened? Er . . . what significant changes took place in western Europe after about AD 1000?'

'Wasn't there more stability?' suggested Kirsty. 'The Viking, Muslim and Magyar invasions petered out, the western Roman Empire was sort of revived, and the Church promoted the Peace and Truce of God.'

'There was growing prosperity,' proclaimed Wade. 'A better climate and improved agricultural techniques supported a growing population with greater demand for consumer goods. Travel became easier, which encouraged trade and commerce, and towns grew in size and importance . . .'

'But they weren't as big as modern cities,' volunteered Maureen, 'and they were cramped and dirty. I read that you just chucked your rubbish out into the street.'

'Most unsanitary,' remarked Melinda.

'It was certainly a period of expansion,' put in Ruth. 'Hundreds of monasteries sprang up all over Europe, and the crusades took western Europeans far from their homes to the Middle East.'

'And people were challenged by new ideas, attitudes and values,' exclaimed Christobel. 'There was what Chenu has called "a hunger of the spirit", a greater awareness of the possibility of progress, and there were simply marvellous advances in philosophy, theology, law, art, architecture, literature, and so on.'

'Er . . . yes,' agreed Derek. 'Which particular medieval scholars did you come across in your reading?'

'One of my favourite medieval scholars is St Anselm,' revealed Ruth. 'He was Abbot of Bec from 1078 to 1093 and Archbishop of Canterbury from 1093 until 1109. In spite of all the duties that these posts must have entailed he still found time for meditation, study and devotional and theological writings. He applied all his intellect and reasoning to seeking God, but he never lost sight of the fact that God is ultimately above human comprehension: "that than which nothing greater can be thought". He wrote:

Lord, I am not trying to make my way to your height, for my understanding is in no way equal to that, but I do desire to understand a little of your truth which my heart already believes and loves. I do not seek to understand so that I may believe, but I believe so that I may understand . . .

'However, what I love most about him is his guidance on prayer. In his time the monastic tradition of prayer based on a continuous, orderly recitation of the Psalter was adopted by some lay Christians, but as always, I suppose, there seems to have been a growing desire among religious and laity alike for a more intimate, personal relationship with God. Anselm helped promote a new tradition of personal prayer:

> Yield room for some little time to God; and rest for a little time in him. Enter the inner chamber of your mind; shut out all thoughts except that of God, and such as can help you in seeking him; close your door and seek him. Speak now, my whole heart! Speak now to God, saying, "I seek your face; your face, Lord, will I seek. And come now, Lord my God, teach my heart where and how it may seek you, where and how it may find you."

'Unfortunately, his influence on theology was even more significant,' said Wade in a dampening voice. 'According to his "satisfaction" theory, all humans are sinful and deserve punishment. They have an obligation to make the satisfaction required by God's justice system, but not the power to do so. God, on the other hand, has the power but not the obligation. Solution: the God-man, Jesus Christ, paid the satisfaction due to God for human sin.'

'Which is absolutely frightful theology!' cried Christobel. 'God is just like a harsh, legalistic, feudal lord. Sin offends his honour, so satisfaction has to be made. What about his love and mercy?'

'God is always loving and merciful, but he is also always

just,' replied Melinda in a reproving tone. 'He is totally opposed to sin and cannot tolerate or condone it. Fortunately, his mercy makes him want to redeem us, and he has provided a way through Christ's obedience which culminated in his death on the cross . . .'

'Romans 5:19: "For just as through the disobedience of the one man [Adam] the many were made sinners, so also through the obedience of the one man [Jesus] the many will be made righteous,"' quoted Frank.

'I believe that the Bible alone is sufficient for Christians,' declared Melinda, 'but I acknowledge that throughout history men like Anselm have helped us understand our faith better, and they are, therefore, worthy of study.'

'I'm not a fan of the "satisfaction" theory,' said Ruth, 'but I have to admit that it's an improvement on earlier theories which explained our Lord's death in terms of ransom paid to the devil. However, I prefer Abelard's emphasis on God's love rather than his honour and justice: Jesus did not die to appease God's anger but to inspire humans through an example of faithful love.'

'Peter Abelard was a bit younger than Anselm,' pointed out Derek. 'He lived from . . . er . . . 1079 to 1144, and he became one of the most famous teachers associated with the cathedral school in Paris. Er . . . what were the cathedral schools?'

'Before 1050 a good education was available to few, outside monasteries,' answered Ruth, 'but by 1100 masters attached to cathedrals were attracting pupils. They taught the seven liberal arts (grammar, dialectic, rhetoric, arithmetic, geometry, astronomy and music), and theology to advanced students. Grammar and dialectic may sound boring but they introduced students to the Christian and secular classics and taught them how to think and argue accurately and critically.'

'Abelard, in particular, strove to examine Christian writings methodically,' swept on Wade. 'In his famous *Sic et Non* (*Yes and No*) he assembled a list of questions, such as "Is God all-powerful or not?" He then quoted texts from the Bible, the works of the Church Fathers, and decrees of popes and councils. Some supported the "yes" side, and some the "no". Abelard seems to have believed that the contradictions could be rationally explained, but he did not attempt to demonstrate how.'

'Which just left people more confused than ever,' said Maureen. 'I think Abelard was a real arrogant so-and-so. He seduced Heloise, got her pregnant and then didn't want to marry her because it would harm his career! He ended up dumping her in a nunnery. Typical selfish male!'

'Heloise was very beautiful and extremely intelligent,' sighed Christobel. 'Abelard was employed by her uncle to teach her because she was so brilliant. While studying side by side they fell in love. I think that Abelard was frightfully self-centred and conceited, Maureen, but it was actually Heloise who nobly insisted that he concentrate on his studies without publicly acknowledging their secret marriage, which could damage his reputation.'

'Well, Heloise's uncle got his revenge!' sniggered Jason.

'How?' asked Kirsty naïvely.

'He ensured that Abelard could not have any more children,' said Christobel delicately.

Jason, as usual, was more direct. 'He hired a gang of thugs who cut his genitals off, but,' Jason continued in a squeaky voice, 'Abelard went on teaching and attracted many pupils.'

'He was, not surprisingly, very controversial,' said Wade coolly, 'and some of his opinions were condemned by the Church. Nevertheless, he is regarded as one of the pioneers of scholasticism, the quest for logical formulation of the Christian faith. Thus theology became an academic discipline in which doctrine was analysed, defined and codified.

Logical reasoning was, of course, extended to other fields of thought, but characteristic of the Middle Ages was the attempt to fit all knowledge into a Christian framework.'

This prompted Ruth to disclose that the greatest scholastic theologian/philosopher was undoubtedly Thomas Aquinas, whose *Summa Theologiae* is like an enormous encyclopaedic summary of Christian thought. It contains 512 questions, almost 3,000 articles, and over 1,000 objections and replies.

'But a few months before he died in 1274 Thomas confessed that "all that I have written seems like straw to me",' said Christobel. 'Isn't that sad?'

'Well, he didn't stick to the Bible, but got carried away with a lot of Aristotelian philosophy which had just been rediscovered in the West,' said Frank. 'And as a result the Catholic Church still bases its teaching more on a pagan Greek than the Word of God.'

'Er . . . actually, Christobel, the context in which Thomas made his remark about his work seeming like straw is important,' intervened Derek uncomfortably. 'It was in 1273, just after he had had a mystical experience during a celebration of the Eucharist.'

Christobel thoroughly understood how such an experience could completely cast into the shade all attempts at academic theologizing.

'When was he canonized?' asked Jason. 'It must have been pretty soon after he died because his body was boiled to remove the flesh so that his bones could be distributed as relics!'

Kirsty shuddered.

'Guilds or "universal societies" of teachers and scholars emerged in the late twelfth century to better organize the growing number of students desiring an education, and to license suitable people to teach,' intervened Derek once more. 'The University of Paris, where Thomas taught, was one of the first of these new educational institutions. It had faculties specializing in ... er ... arts, law, medicine and theology. Oxford and Cambridge followed soon afterwards, while Bologna in Italy became particularly famous for its school of law.'

The study of canon and civil law was stimulated by the conflict between the papacy and the empire in the eleventh century,' Wade informed us. 'Supporters of the papacy searched through papal and conciliar legislation to find evidence to support their case, and royalists, in turn, rediscovered ancient Roman secular law. And along with the study of law came the growth of civil and ecclesiastical courts. Ecclesiastical courts dealt with matters relating to marriage, wills, religious observance and public morality. Rome became the final court of appeal, and a large and very expensive papal bureaucracy developed to handle the business that flowed there as a result.'

'Henry II, King of England and ruler of most of western France in the twelfth century, was greatly interested in law and order,' pronounced Melinda. 'He hired many lawyers, built up an efficient government administration, and developed English common law ...'

'What's that got to do with church history?' interrupted Jason, reverting to his squeaky voice.

'If you will allow me to continue,' glared Melinda, 'I will tell you that Henry came into conflict with the insufferable Thomas Becket, Archbishop of Canterbury, because Becket, among other things, quite unreasonably refused to allow clergy charged with criminal offences to be tried in the royal courts. As it happened, Becket was murdered by four of Henry's over-enthusiastic knights. It was most regrettable because it made him a martyr in the eyes of the ignorant masses. A cult developed around him, and pilgrimages to Canterbury became very popular.'

'Oh, yes,' said Jason. 'The monks at Canterbury collected the blood and brains which gushed out from his head when he was killed and mixed them with water so that they could put drops on the tongues of pilgrims. All kinds of miracles then occurred. The blind received sight, the lame were healed, even the dead were raised!'

'They probably weren't really dead,' commented Wade, 'just unconscious. Medieval medical knowledge was so primitive that half the time it wasn't known whether people were really dead or not. I wonder how many people were buried alive? Anyway, the monks at Canterbury obviously made the most of supposed miracles and heavily promoted the shrine because they made a fortune out of it.'

'That must have really annoyed Henry II,' remarked Maureen.

'He was all right,' said Jason with a grin. 'He did penance at Thomas's tomb and was rewarded with victory in his war against Scotland.'

'From what I read, Henry's son John was nasty, rude, unscrupulous, greedy, unforgiving and immoral,' said Maureen, never one to mince words. 'What with all that, and military defeat, high taxation and being excommunicated by Pope Innocent III because he refused to accept Innocent's friend Simon Langton as Archbishop of Canterbury, he wasn't too popular. So there was a general uprising in 1215 and John was forced to issue the Magna Charta, which is supposed to be the basis of England's parliamentary constitution. He also had to accept the Pope as a sort of feudal overlord, and pay him lots of taxes, because Innocent wasn't letting English priests baptize, marry or bury anyone in England, which I think was real unfair. I don't see why the ordinary people had to suffer for John's sins.'

'England was placed under an interdict,' explained Derek,

'which means that public worship was suspended but . . . er
. . . sacraments like baptism and absolution of the dying could
still be administered privately to individuals.'

'The power of the medieval papacy reached its peak during
Innocent's pontificate,' said Melinda tartly. 'He even elevated
himself to "vicar of Christ" instead of "vicar of St Peter", which
other popes had claimed to be. And he made other outrageous
statements, for example: "The Pope is lower than God but
higher than man", and "A secular king is to the Pope what the
moon is to sun." He continually meddled in European politics
and clearly wanted to establish a papal monarchy and dominate
"Christendom" . . .' Melinda broke off with a fit of coughing.

'He was only thirty when he became a cardinal, and thirty-
seven when he became pope,' piped up Kirsty. 'I thought
popes were always old men.'

'Perhaps thirty-seven was old then,' suggested Jason. 'If
he'd been a peasant, he probably would have been dead!'

'But I read that his predecessor was in his nineties when he
died', I managed to put in quickly, 'so it was quite a change.
He was apparently a great statesman and Church reformer,
really interested in scholarship and pastoral care. He also
convoked the Fourth Lateran Council which began in 1215
and was the greatest church council in the Middle Ages.'

I avoided meeting Melinda's eyes.

'Over 400 bishops and 800 abbots took part in the council,'
said Ruth, giving me an encouraging smile. 'One poor old
bishop was actually trampled to death in the rush to enter the
church of the Lateran on the first day. Eventually a lot of
legislation was passed concerning the fight against heresy
and the reform of the Church.'

Derek agreed, and said that we will be considering
Innocent's attitude to heresy and the mendicant orders in a
few weeks' time.

'Nevertheless,' maintained Melinda rather hoarsely, 'Innocent only became so powerful because of the weaknesses of the secular rulers of his day, and, in particular, the political turmoil in England, Germany and Italy.'

'Emperor Henry VI died in 1197, just before Innocent became pope, and his three-year-old son Frederick became King of Sicily,' related Jason. 'Innocent made sure that Fred got a really good education, and that he became emperor in 1211. However, he soon discovered that he had nursed a viper in his bosom. Fred couldn't care less about Christianity, or his lands in northern Europe. He preferred to live by the Mediterranean, uncomfortably close to Rome. He turned Sicily into the most efficiently organized state in Europe, and his court became by far the most brilliant and cosmopolitan. He welcomed Jewish and Arabic scholars, and kept a zoo of exotic animals and a harem of Muslim women guarded by eunuchs. He even hired Muslim mercenaries to fight against Christian cities in Italy, and he went on a "crusade" to the Middle East where he negotiated a treaty with the Sultan of Egypt. This gave him control of Jerusalem, but, as part of the deal, he guaranteed Muslims and Jews freedom of worship. It was the most successful crusading venture of the century but the Pope was outraged. He couldn't work out whether Fred was an atheist or a Muslim. It was painfully obvious that he wasn't a good Catholic!'

'He must have been corrupted by Arabic culture,' said Frank. 'But I thought that we were supposed to be talking about the twelfth century, not the thirteenth.'

'There has been considerable debate about when the Renaissance began and when it ended,' replied Derek. 'I think it probably ... er ... started with the monastic and papal reform movements in the eleventh century, and reached its peak in the early thirteenth with the ... er ... Fourth Lateran Council, the Magna Charta, the beginning of the mendicant orders and ... er ... the rise of the universities.'

'The rest of the thirteenth century witnessed a conspicuous decline,' battled on Melinda, looking quite unwell. 'The conflict between successive popes and Frederick II greatly undermined the empire and discredited the papacy.'

'Is there anything else that anyone would like to say about the medieval Renaissance?' said Derek, glancing at his watch.

'We haven't discussed Gothic art and architecture yet,' exclaimed Christobel. 'Thousands of absolutely wonderful churches and cathedrals were built, with magnificent pillars and vaults and stained glass windows. The Church of Saint-Denis in Paris, built in the mid-twelfth century, was one of the first Gothic buildings. The Abbot of Saint-Denis said that when it was finished, "I seemed to find myself, as it were, in some strange part of the universe which was neither wholly of the baseness of the earth, nor wholly of the serenity of heaven, but by the grace of God I seemed lifted in a mystic manner from this lower towards that upper sphere ..."'

'And cathedrals and churches were stuffed with statues and pictures,' said Maureen, 'so that people who couldn't read the Bible could at least get some idea of what it was about. And they had to burn incense everywhere to try to disguise the peasants' stink.'

'Church services, with all the ceremony and ritual, must have been wonderful events in the otherwise dreary lives of the peasants,' commented Christobel. 'Saints' days, feast days, processions and liturgical plays would have been especially special. The nobility, of course, had the concept of chivalry and courtly love poetry, and that really drew on an amazing amount of religious imagery. Legends about King Arthur's quest for the Holy Grail were frightfully popular ...'

'I'm afraid that many courtly love poems are based on pagan myths and are consequently quite immoral,' interjected Melinda. 'They always seem to be about adulterous affairs between knights and married women...'

'I read part of a poem about a count's son who fell in love with a beautiful slave girl who turned out to be a king's daughter,' said Jason. 'It was like a medieval soap opera. At one stage the lover was warned that if he went to bed with her he'd go to hell instead of heaven...' Jason flicked through the pages of Rosalind and Christopher Brooke's *Popular Religion in the Middle Ages*. 'Yes, here's his reply:

> What would I do in heaven? I have no wish to enter there, unless I have Nicolette, my own sweet love... For to heaven go only such people as I'll tell you of: all those doddering priests... and the folk garbed in rags and tatters... These are the ones who go to heaven, and I want nothing to do with them. Nay, I would go to hell; for to hell go the pretty clerks and the fine knights killed in tournaments and splendid wars... I want to go along with these. And there too go the lovely ladies, gently bred and mannered, those who have had two lovers or three besides their lords, and there go gold and silver, and silk and sable...'

'That's the perennial excuse put forward by non-Christians for their sins!' interjected Melinda, incensed. ' "Hell will be more fun." If they only read the Bible...'

'They'd find out that there is not much fun about a lake of burning fire,' finished Frank with gruesome relish.

Melinda gathered her belongings and declared that she was going home to lie down. Derek politely said that he hoped that she would feel better soon.

'And I hope that she hasn't spread her germs everywhere,' muttered Maureen as Melinda went out the door. 'My daughter's baby is due in six weeks' time, and I don't want to pass anything on to her.'

I left Christobel insisting that Maureen try some garlic and horseradish tablets which she has found to be absolutely wonderful.

Before I could get far Kirsty stopped me and, after some hesitation, shyly disclosed that she joined a Christian youth group a few weeks ago. I tried to sound supportive because I know that she has had trouble making new friends since she moved to the city from the country. Eventually she confided that the youth group is hosting an 'all-you-can-eat-pizza night' next Friday. Each member is expected to bring along at least one non-Christian friend. The idea is that the non-Christian will initially be attracted by the pizza, but then be inspired by a special guest speaker, an evangelist.

'I told Neil, our group leader, that I really didn't know any non-Christians that I could invite,' Kirsty told me, 'but he insisted that I find someone. Suddenly, in the tutorial just now, I had a thought – could I ask Jason?'

She wanted to know my opinion. I had to admit that I didn't like her chances, especially after Jason's negative experiences at Frank's Prayer, Praise and Holy Power rally recently, but I supposed that it couldn't do any harm to ask him. As Jason was still talking to Derek, Kirsty decided to take the bull by the horns (so to speak) and go up to him before her courage ran out. I waited to hear the results. She came back looking relieved. 'At first he seemed sort of suspicious, and he asked if there'd be any singing or talking in tongues, but when I said that I was sure there wouldn't be, he said that he'd go anywhere for free pizza. I don't suppose', she added bashfully, 'that you could come as well – for moral support?'

I am not really a youth group type of person, but I couldn't resist the appealing look in Kirsty's eyes – and I do like pizza, too!

WEEK·NINE

New religious orders

'Er . . . the early medieval period has sometimes been called the "Benedictine centuries",' began Derek rather tentatively, 'because the Benedictine Rule was so popular and influential, but from the . . . er . . . late eleventh century a myriad of new forms of religious life emerged. What examples could you find?'

'What I can't understand,' said Maureen, 'is why, just when things were getting better (no more invasions, growth of towns, and all that), people went off in droves to become dirty, smelly hermits. Some writer connected with the papal reform movement (I forget his name) wrote . . . now, where did I jot it down? Oh, yes, here it is. Lawrence quotes it on page 131 of *Medieval Monasticism:* "Who would not be astounded at seeing men previously dressed in silken and golden robes, escorted by cohorts of servants, and accustomed to all the pleasures of affluence, now content with a single cloak, enclosed, barefooted, unkempt, and so parched and wasted by abstinence?" They must have been mad.'

'What I cannot comprehend is how such behaviour could possibly have been thought to honour God and further his service,' commented Melinda.

'Well, they were trying to get back to the way of life of the desert Fathers of the early Church,' said Frank. 'You know, those nut cases who went to live by themselves in caves, eat grass, sit on poles, and goodness knows what else. But it clearly wasn't biblical.'

'The ... er ... return to primitive ideals was certainly an important part of the eleventh- and twelfth-century Renaissance,' intervened Derek, 'but the lifestyle of the hermits of this time was generally not quite the same as that of the early ascetics.'

I don't think that there was such a great emphasis on solitude,' said Ruth. 'Although hermits usually retired to remote places, more often than not they seem to have gone with companions, not alone ...'

'They rejected the growth in urban life and the burgeoning money economy, and went into the "desert" in search of renewal and a way to meet the new challenges posed by society,' lectured Wade. 'They displayed great concern for Gospel values, especially sharing the experience of poverty with the poor, and engaging in practical measures of assistance (such as setting up hospices). Preaching the Gospel was also very important to them.'

'Like that Peter-the-Hermit person who preached the First Crusade,' said Maureen. 'Fat lot of good that did.'

'But hermits didn't belong to religious orders, and aren't they what we are supposed to be looking at today?' asked Frank.

'But as groups of hermits grew in size, rules and regulations for community life were drawn up,' answered Ruth, 'and hence orders evolved. One of the most famous was the Carthusian Order, founded in 1084 by a hermit. It preserved a mixture of solitary and community life. Monks lived in separate cells, each with its own little garden plot and latrine, but they met regularly for worship in the church.'

'And the only time that they were allowed to talk was for a

little time on Sunday afternoons, and some special festival days,' interjected Maureen. 'I just know that if I had to live like that I'd spend all week thinking of things to say and then promptly forget them when I had the opportunity to speak. It must have been real frustrating.'

'I hardly think that it was a way of life conducive to good health and spreading the Gospel,' declared Melinda.

'They worked in their gardens to exercise their bodies, and they made books in their cells to exercise their minds,' responded Ruth. 'In fact, the first prior believed that making books, especially the Bible, served a missionary purpose – it was a way of disseminating the Word of God.'

'The . . . er . . . Carthusians never attracted large numbers of recruits, but the order slowly developed and maintained a reputation for sanctity throughout the medieval period,' put in Derek quickly. 'Michael, what religious order did you read about?'

Put on the spot I managed to blurt out something about the Augustinian canons. They seemed to have been clerical monks. Their pattern of life was based on a letter St Augustine wrote to his sister, who lived in a religious community, which gave general advice on things like sharing possessions and obeying a superior. From the late eleventh century communities which claimed to follow some version of this "rule" sprang up all over Europe.

'Houses of Augustinian canons were generally cheaper to establish than Benedictine monasteries, so the lesser nobility and upper middle class could afford to found them and become their patrons, receiving in return things like prayers for their souls,' observed Wade knowingly.

'Augustinian canons also attempted to recover the life-style of the primitive Church and live like the Christian community described in Acts 2,' added Ruth.

'But the Christians in Acts 2 weren't monks or canons,' maintained Frank.

'The monks and canons of the twelfth century didn't think so,' said Wade. 'They certainly assumed that they were living an apostolic life.'

'But a key characteristic of an apostolic life is evangelism,' said Melinda firmly, 'which seems to have been conspicuously lacking from the so-called "religious" life of the Middle Ages.'

'Not always,' protested Ruth. 'Some of the Augustinian canons, for example, placed great emphasis on preaching and pastoral work. They also ran schools, hospitals, and refuges for the blind and lepers.'

'Another religious order that got going at the end of the eleventh century was the Cistercians,' contributed Maureen. 'The Abbey of Citeaux was started in 1098 by Robert, Abbot of somewhere else, and some of his monks who wanted to get back to a much stricter interpretation of the Benedictine Rule than was usually the case at the time. They were really into poverty, simplicity and manual labour. Can't understand why, unless it was some kind of reaction to the Cluniacs who were spending all their time praying in their elaborate churches, poor things. Anyway, I started reading *The Cistercian World: Monastic Writings of the Twelfth Century*. According to some early chronicles, Citeaux was a place "where men rarely penetrated and none but wild things lived, so densely covered was it then with woodland and thornbush". It sounds awful, but the first monks were really pleased with it because they wanted to shun the world. They weren't going to have churches and ovens and mills which peasants could use, and they weren't going to allow lay people to be buried in their monastery which lots of other monasteries did because that way they got donations and burial fees. They also didn't want relics which would attract hordes of pilgrims. It was all going to be very harsh and austere. But then the chronicle says that they all became very sad because no one came to join them. As a matter of fact, "almost everyone seeing and hearing of the exceptional and almost unheard-of harshness of their life, instead of drawing near, made haste to put heart and body at a distance." Can you blame them? At least some people had some sense.

'Yet the Cistercians went on to experience phenomenal growth, greater than any other order,' pointed out Derek. 'By 1200 there were over 500 Cistercian monasteries in existence. What do you think caused this?'

'Stephen Harding, an Englishman, was Abbot of Citeaux from 1109 and things seemed to pick up from then,' said Wade.

'And in 1112 or 1113 a young nobleman called Bernard entered Citeaux, and he became abbot of its daughter house, Clairvaux, in 1115,' revealed Ruth. 'He was a brilliant preacher and spiritual theologian, and he attracted many recruits, a number of whom went on to become abbots, bishops and cardinals, and one even became pope. So great was his influence over kings and popes that it has been said that Bernard virtually became the uncrowned ruler of Europe. By the time he died in 1153 he had established seventy monasteries and had an additional ninety under his authority.'

'He was so good a preacher that mothers had to lock up their sons, and wives their husbands, when he went on a recruiting tour,' commented Maureen, 'which I think was real sad, although as far as I am concerned he could have had my husband, and good riddance. He also dragged most of his family into his order, but I reckon that he might have lived to regret that. The chronicler says that he performed lots of miracles, but no matter how amazing these were, his uncle and brother always found something to criticize. Where did I see ...? Oh, yes, page 35: "They certainly did not spare him, finding fault with his shyness, carping also at things well done, dismissive of seeming miracles and reducing that most gentle of men (who never said a word in contradiction) to tears with their taunts and reproaches." I know just how he must have felt. My older sister will never admit that I can do or have anything better than her. When I bought a new television set she said that the model I had chosen always breaks down...'

'Did anyone else have anything they wanted to say about Bernard?' inquired Derek.

'It says somewhere in *The Cistercian World* that "his keenest desire, his greatest joy was the harvest of souls and the conversion of sinners",' said Frank. 'At least he was on the right track there.'

'He was very gentle to birds and animals,' contributed Kirsty enthusiastically, 'and the chronicler says that many times on a journey he would save with a sign of the cross a hare that was fleeing from hounds.'

'And another thing that I have just remembered', went on Maureen, 'was that he had a weak stomach and bowels. All he could eat was a mouthful of bread softened with water and a little broth. When my peptic ulcer plays up that's all I can eat, too, or milk arrowroot biscuits dunked in warm milk.'

'Funny that he couldn't heal himself although he supposedly healed hundreds of other people,' remarked Jason. 'On a preaching tour to promote the Second Crusade the blind reportedly received sight, and the deaf, dumb and crippled had whatever was wrong with them fixed. Bernard saw the miracles as proof of God's approval for the crusade, but if any really did occur, they were probably due to the mass hysteria and emotion generated by the great crowds curing problems that were psychosomatic anyway.'

'I think that it was frightful the way Bernard used his great talent for preaching to persuade people to go on the Second Crusade,' said Christobel crossly. 'He even boasted afterwards that he left whole towns and castles empty, and deprived many women of their husbands. And it was all to no avail because the Second Crusade was an utter, tragic failure.'

'There is evidence that he only preached the crusade at the insistence of the Pope,' murmured Ruth. 'He loved his monastery so much that he hated leaving it.'

'Well, he didn't have to encourage the Knights Templars,' insisted Christobel. 'He was practically their founder, and he told them that "to kill someone else for the sake of Christ or to wish to undergo death is not only completely free of sin, but even highly praiseworthy and meritable". How can someone who thought like that possibly be regarded as a saint?'

'It doesn't seem a very appropriate thing for a saint to say today,' admitted Ruth, 'but I suppose that it reflects the mentality of the time. And the Templars weren't totally bad. One of their major functions was to protect pilgrims journeying to the Holy Land. Pilgrims were apparently being attacked, robbed and even killed. Like Cistercian monks, the Templars lived in chastity, simplicity and poverty, with no personal possessions. I think that by encouraging the order to develop Bernard hoped that idle young knights would be diverted from private warfare and tournaments and hunting to more worthwhile pursuits.'

'There's absolutely nothing worthwhile about warfare in any form,' maintained Christobel stubbornly. 'But by proclaiming that there was Bernard influenced the formation of the Teutonic Knights in Germany, and they took part in evangelism by the sword around the Baltic and bequeathed to

Germany a frightful heritage of militarism and pseudo-religious military symbolism. And other nations are not exempt from that either! Just think of the crosses that are awarded for military valour by Great Britain and the United States. Horrible! Horrible!' Christobel gave a melodramatic shudder.

Melinda then took the opportunity to point out that the military orders became wealthy and corrupt, and the Cistercians became very wealthy and declined as well.

'Their policy of going off to remote areas and engaging in manual labour paid great dividends,' declared Wade. 'The Cistercians were at the forefront of agricultural advances, and as they couldn't channel their profits into elaborate buildings or a luxurious lifestyle, they resorted to buying more and more land, which in turn increased their revenues. Unfortunately, there is evidence that they were not above displacing peasants from the land in the process, and hence they contributed to the growing number of poor people living in urban areas.'

'They were also frightfully misogynistic,' proclaimed Christobel. 'They tried not to start any convents for women, and one abbot said . . .' She flicked through the pages of R. W. Southern's *Western Society and the Church in the Middle Ages.* 'Oh, he actually belonged to another order, the Order of the Premonstratensian Canons, but it was founded about the same time as the Cistercians and was practically the same:

We and our whole community of canons, recognizing that the wickedness of women is greater than all the other wickedness of the world, and that there is no anger like that of women, and the poison of asps and dragons is more curable and less dangerous to men than the familiarity of women, have unanimously decreed for the safety of our souls, no less than for that of our bodies and goods, that we will on no account receive any more sisters to the increase of our perdition, but will avoid them like poisonous animals.

Isn't that appalling! And after quoting this Southern goes on to say that there was "no religious body more thoroughly masculine in its temper and discipline than the Cistercians, none that shunned female contact with greater determination, or raised more formidable barriers against the intrusion of women". Yet in spite of this convents sprang up all over Europe which claimed to follow the Cistercian way of life. In fact, before long there were more Cistercian convents for women than abbeys for men! And when the pompous male abbots eventually (and grudgingly) decided to take control of the women's houses and discipline them, the women more often than not told them in no uncertain terms that they were not welcome and would not be heeded. Served them right!'

'I think that Gilbert of Sempringham tried at one stage in the early twelfth century to get the Cistercians to take over a convent which he had established, but they refused,' reflected Ruth, 'and hence the Gilbertine Order developed in its own right. Gilbert was a priest, the son of a wealthy Norman knight, and he had originally wanted to set up a religious community for men, but no men would submit to him and seven young village girls volunteered instead.'

'I read that he shut them up in a building next to the church at Sempringham,' said Kirsty in an awed voice, 'and they were never allowed out and no one was allowed in. Food and things they needed had to be passed in through a window because there was only one door and Gilbert kept it locked all the time and only he was allowed to have a key.'

'No man would get my key,' muttered Maureen.

'The Gilbertine nuns ended up having canons and lay brothers attached to their convents to deal with business matters,' recounted Jason. 'The men and women weren't supposed to meet but at Watton Priory in Yorkshire the men had to enter the women's section to do some kind of job, and a young girl who had been stuck in the priory since she was four years old saw one of them and fell in love. They somehow managed to meet secretly and as a result the girl became pregnant. The nuns, when they found out about this, beat her and imprisoned her in chains in a cell and fed her only bread and water. Then they got hold of her lover and took him into the cell and forced the girl to cut off his penis which they stuffed down her throat . . .'

'I think that we have heard enough,' said Melinda glaring at Jason. 'There is no need to go into such revolting details.'

'What happened to the baby?' asked Kirsty, looking horrified.

'A miracle occurred,' replied Jason with a grin. 'One morning, when the girl was close to giving birth, the nuns went to the cell where she was still chained up and found no sign of the baby at all. They poked and prodded and squeezed her breasts but there was nothing to indicate that she had had the child or was still pregnant. Eventually she explained that while she was asleep she had dreamt that a deceased archbishop whom she had known had visited her with two women and taken the baby away. The nuns didn't know what to do, but they kept her in chains until the chains miraculously fell off. Then they consulted a famous Cistercian monk, who concluded that God must have intervened. But this didn't stop the scandal becoming known, and it resulted in a stricter separation of the sexes in Gilbertine houses.'

'Women should not have needed men to handle their

business affairs at all,' said Christobel in a lofty tone. 'Hildegard of Bingen lived in a community of women attached to a Benedictine monastery but she eventually managed to break free from the monks and establish her own convent. She was an amazing woman! She had the most wonderful visions, and a real prophetic gift. In 1141, when she was forty-two, she experienced the heavens opening and "a blinding light of exceptional brilliance" flowed through her brain and she suddenly understood the meaning of the Bible. In response to a divine command she recorded her visions in several books. She also wrote saints' lives and theological commentaries, and, wait for this, books on natural history and medicine! Hence she has been called Germany's first woman doctor and scientist. In addition, she was a very talented poet, artist and musician, and she corresponded with popes, emperors, bishops and abbots, including Bernard of Clairvaux, who gave her encouragement when she was not sure whether to publish her visions or not. She also performed lots of miracles and went on preaching tours – often preaching in monasteries, which was a rare privilege for a woman . . .'

'Hildegard was an exceptional woman,' interjected Wade, cutting short Christobel's enthusiastic account of her, 'but (like Bernard) she was very much a product of her times. We all know that good scholarship is based on 1 per cent inspiration and 99 per cent perspiration, but the only way that Hildegard could gain credibility as a female scholar was by claiming that in her case it was the other way around. And, unfortunately, she only admitted aristocratic girls to her convent, and defended this on the grounds that hierarchical states are willed by God, and you would not put oxen, sheep, asses and goats in the one enclosure.'

'That's one of the things I don't like about medieval

nunneries,' said Maureen. 'It seems that most of them were pretty well exclusively for the upper classes, and they could be used as dumping grounds for unmarried daughters, heiresses whose guardians didn't want them to inherit their wealth, and poor girls whose fathers were defeated in battle.'

'Yes, well . . . er . . . we will have a special tutorial on medieval women in a few weeks' time,' concluded Derek. 'The purpose of today's tutorial was to discover something of the diversity and richness of religious life in the twelfth century . . .'

'Well, I am afraid that I have not discovered anything that was not unnecessary or downright abhorrent,' stated Melinda. 'Apart from anything else, it was most unedifying to read about the conflicts between the different religious orders. The Cistercians, for example, claimed that the Cluniacs were worldly and lax, while the Cluniacs accused the Cistercians of being a new breed of Pharisees, and both maintained that the monastic life was preferable to that of the canons, who, of course, argued that the opposite was the case.'

'I still can't understand how people could actually want to become monks, nuns, canons, or whatever,' said Maureen, 'or dump their children in monasteries. But lots apparently did. The countryside was dotted with monasteries. Thank goodness monasticism has waned today is all I can say.'

'It hasn't totally died out,' remarked Ruth dryly. 'Taizé testifies to that.'

'What is Taizé?' asked Kirsty.

'A religious community founded by the son of a Swiss Reformed pastor in France during the Second World War,' replied Ruth. 'It is actually close to the site of Cluny. It has contributed greatly to the ecumenical movement.'

'And I just adore Taizé chants,' cried Christobel. 'We sing

them in my church all the time. When you stop to think about it, religious communities have enriched the Church so much through their spiritual writings, guidance on prayer, music, and all that. And it's amazing the way ripples can spread way beyond the confines of a single monastery, geographically and chronologically. I wonder if Hildegard of Bingen ever imagined that people would be inspired by her writings 800 years after her death?' On this thought-provoking note we all got up to leave.

'Well, there's no way that I'd take vows of poverty, chastity and obedience,' said Jason to me on the way out. He then gave Kirsty a wink and thanked her for inviting him to the youth group 'all-you-can-eat-pizza evening' last Friday. He'd had a fantastic night. Strangely enough, Kirsty didn't look very pleased. I apologized for not being able to stay for the whole programme and said that Jason certainly seemed to be enjoying himself when I left. He was chatting to an attractive girl with blue eyes and long, blonde hair.

'That was Leanne,' said Kirsty in a quavering voice, 'Neil the group leader's girlfriend. He's been trying to lead her to Christ for months now, and he hoped that last Friday would be the big night.'

'And it wasn't?' I inquired, sensing something wrong.

'Neil had to tidy up the hall after the meeting so Jason drove Leanne home.'

'What's wrong with that?' I blustered. 'Quite thoughtful of Jason.'

'Yes, but when Neil visited Leanne the next morning, to ask what she thought of the guest speaker, JASON WAS STILL THERE!'

I was beginning to get an inkling of the problem. Neil had hoped that Leanne would discover Jesus, and she'd found Jason instead.

'Neil is devastated,' wailed poor Kirsty, 'and he blames me for inviting Jason. But I thought that we were supposed to invite non-Christians and sinners. I'm never going back to that youth group again – NEVER!'

Took Kirsty to the refectory and bought her a cup of tea. Love can sure complicate things at times.

WEEK·TEN

Heresy

Poor Melinda was still coughing when we met for this week's tutorial and Derek had almost lost his voice. However, I was quite looking forward to our discussion. I had found an envelope in my letter-box marked 'top secret'. Inside were instructions from Jason: I was to come as Pope Alexander III!

Read as much as I could about Alexander. He was an Italian aristocrat who studied canon law and became one of the foremost teachers of law in Bologna. He was elected pope in 1159 and died in 1181. I couldn't find a suitable costume, but Jason bounded into the room wearing a long back academic gown and a clerical collar. He announced that he was an inquisitor.

'Right, now, peasants. I've come to preach you a sermon. You'd better listen good. Heresy comes from the ancient Greek word *haeresis* which means choice. However, you're all too stupid to know right from wrong, so the Church decides for you. You've gotta believe what the Church tells you, even if it's utter crap and doesn't make sense, because otherwise you'll ROT IN HELL. Got that? Now, I have a strong suspicion that some of you think that you know better than the Church. What arrogance! Nevertheless, because I am such a nice Christian priest, I'll give you a chance to confess your horrible sin. You'll then receive a little penance to satisfy God's justice system. You might have to fast for a few days, go on a pilgrimage, or wear a yellow cross stitched to your clothing. Oh, and by the way, I'll want to know the names of every other possible heretic you've ever come into contact with, dead or alive!'

Jason looked around inquiringly. 'No takers? Well, is there anyone here who isn't a heretic but would like to rat on someone who is . . . er . . . assist me in my inquiries? Know any juicy gossip? Got a grudge against anyone? They needn't know that it was you who betrayed them. If everyone would just close their eyes for a moment . . .'

'He looks suspicious to me,' said Maureen, pointing to Frank who was sitting clutching a Good News Bible.

Jason pounced on the Bible. 'Good heavens, a Bible in the ordinary language of the people!' he exclaimed in horror. 'They might actually READ it! They might discover that Jesus was a humble carpenter, not a wealthy, powerful pope, and his first followers were fishermen, not bishops and monks! We can't have such subversive literature available to the laity! What is your name? he asked Frank in a deep, threatening voice.

'Peter Waldo,' said Frank.

'And who are you, Waldo?' interrogated Jason.

'I think I am . . . no, I was a wealthy merchant from Lyons in France,' replied Frank, gradually gaining confidence. 'I was converted in about 1173 when I heard a wandering minstrel sing about St Alexis. He was a rich young man who dumped his bride on his wedding night and went off to beg his way to the Holy Land . . .'

'What a lousy thing to do,' interjected Maureen, glaring at Frank. 'She must have felt rejected, if not downright humiliated.'

'Then I heard the Word of God,' went on Frank hurriedly. 'Matthew 19:21: "If you would be perfect, go, sell your possessions and give to the poor." So I did that, leaving just enough to support my wife, and I put my two daughters into a convent . . .'

'Did you ask them if they wanted to go?' demanded Maureen.

'I don't think so,' admitted Frank.

'Callous pig! Burn him at the stake!' shouted Maureen.

'Lady, I'm afraid that leaving your family ain't proof of heresy,' said Jason. 'Monks do it all the time. Waldo, what happened after you chucked your girls into a nunnery?'

'I got the gospels and other parts of the New Testament translated into French . . . I could read French,' Frank added proudly. 'Then I took a vow of poverty and set off to preach the Word of God. However, the pompous old Archbishop of Lyons wouldn't give me a licence to preach, so I went to see the Pope.'

'Alexander III,' cried Jason. 'Who, by an amazing coincidence, happens to be here today. What, your grace, your holiness, or whatever, did you make of this merchant-come-preacher?'

My big moment. I remembered that I'd read somewhere that Alexander had been reasonably sympathetic to Waldo's cause. He hadn't found him guilty of any doctrinal errors, and he had approved his vow of poverty. However, he had reaffirmed canon law. Waldo had to obtain permission from local church authorities before he could preach in an area.

'Yeah, well, the Archbishop of Lyons still wouldn't budge,' said Frank, after I had blurted out my bit. 'But I had read the gospels. Jesus said "Go into all the world and preach the good news to all creation." (Mark 16:15) Jesus is a higher authority than a pope or an archbishop! I must obey him first.'

'Quite right, too,' agreed Melinda, thus unwittingly attracting Jason's attention to herself.

'Ah ha! Another damned heretic!'

'Peter Waldo was clearly not in the least heretical,' replied Melinda crossly. 'He showed a commendable concern for the Bible and evangelism, in stark contrast to the decadence of the official Church hierarchy. He lived in poverty, while popes and bishops lived in luxury. He taught the Bible, while priests just mumbled mass in Latin . . .'

'Yeah, and I got lots of followers who became known as Waldensians or Poor Men of Lyons,' said Frank with a pleased expression. 'The Catholic Church rejected us, so we eventually rejected it. We realized that you don't need special intercessors between ordinary Christians and God. Any Christian, man or woman, should be able to pray, preach and administer communion. We got rid of all that saints and purgatory rubbish that the Catholic Church carries on about, as well as altars, pilgrimages and indulgences, what are totally unbiblical.'

'Waldensians were clearly the first Protestants,' proclaimed Melinda. 'They helped pave the way for the Reformation, and the movement survives in Europe to the present day.'

'But the medieval Church couldn't allow untrained preachers to wander around Europe unchecked,' intervened Wade. 'It's all very well to say that they only preached the Bible, but the Bible has to be *interpreted*.'

'What a sensible peasant!' cried Jason, slapping Wade on the back. 'If you have any little peccadilloes you'd like to confess, I'll make sure you get an extra lenient penance.'

'I', said Wade coldly, 'am the Pope. Pope Innocent III to be precise. I don't confess to bumptious priests.'

'Forgive me, your popefulness,' exclaimed Jason, throwing himself to the ground to lie prostrate at Wade's feet. 'I forgot that you might be here today, and I didn't recognize you in jeans and a sweater.'

'This is ridiculous,' sniffed Melinda. 'A waste of time. I'm leaving.'

'Oh, no you're not,' said Jason, swiftly rising and pulling some rope from a bag. In an instant he had bound Melinda's arms to her chair. At first she was too shocked to resist. Shock was followed by anger, suppressed into icy dignity.

'Now, tell us who you are,' Jason demanded in a menacing tone.

'Oh, all right, I am supposed to be a Cathar,' replied Melinda bitterly.

'And what are your horrible, naughty beliefs?'

'I . . . they . . . a Cathar,' said Melinda through clenched teeth, 'does not believe in the Trinity.'

'Is that all?' said Jason.

'Isn't that enough!' spat out Melinda.

'What exactly *do* you believe?'

'A Cathar', replied Melinda in frigid tones 'believes that there are two gods. A good god created the spiritual world and an evil god created the material world. Our souls, created by the good god, are imprisoned in bodies created by the evil god. Death will bring no relief. Our souls will be endlessly reincarnated in other evil bodies. However, the good god sent the Christ to reveal a way of salvation. The Christ was pure spirit, he did not have a real human body or really suffer and die. Cathars claim that they belong to the true Church, and they alone know the way to salvation. You have to get baptized in the spirit, by the laying on of hands, which is known as a *consolomentum.*'

'And what shocking, immoral practices do you engage in?' asked Jason eagerly.

'I do not engage in any immoral practices. As a matter of fact, Cathars are noted for their austere lifestyle. Even the name "Cathar" comes from the Greek word for "pure".

Cathars are divided into two classes. The Perfect, who have received the *consolomentum*, live in strict poverty and celibacy. They regard marriage and sexual reproduction as evil, and do not eat any products associated with sexual reproduction, even milk, eggs and cheese. Those who cannot maintain this lifestyle, but serve and obey the Perfect, are known as Believers. They hope to receive the *consolomentum* on their death bed.'

'How boring,' commented the inquisitor in a disappointed tone, 'but clearly subversive because, like the Waldensians, you might convince peasants that you are a hell of a lot holier than most of the Catholic clergy. What do you think of this horrible sect, your popeness?' he asked me.

'Well,' I said, 'I think that when some suspected Cathars were sent to me in the 1160s I decided that it would be better to pardon the guilty than risk harming the innocent.' Christobel applauded loudly.

'Unfortunately, in the latter half of the twelfth century there was a dramatic increase in the number of Cathars, especially in Languedoc in southern France,' declared Wade. 'They were sometimes called Albigensians after the city of Albi. I was very concerned about this because, as pope, I am responsible for all people's souls. I first tried to bring wayward sheep back to the Catholic fold through peaceful methods. I asked Cistercian monks to preach the Catholic truth in Languedoc, and I encouraged a Spanish Augustinian canon, Dominic Guzman, and his bishop to develop a special ministry. They believed that Catholic preaching would be more effective if preachers lived like the Apostles, in simplicity and poverty. Other men joined Dominic, and so began the Dominican friars, or Order of Preachers ...'

'Why were they allowed to live in poverty and preach when I wasn't?' interrupted Frank.

'They were usually very well educated and loyal to the papacy,' responded Wade coolly. 'As a matter of fact, some of the greatest scholars of the late Middle Ages were Dominicans, including the greatest of all, Thomas Aquinas. Anyway, I also removed from office bishops who were corrupt or negligent, and I called local church synods to remind priests of their duties and condemn unacceptable behaviour. However, in 1208 I suffered a great blow. My legate was assassinated in Languedoc. Catholic Christianity was in grave peril. I remembered that St Augustine had come to the conclusion that, although it was better for heretics to return to the Church voluntarily, in some cases coercion can be justified. Faced with the ineffectiveness of persuasion, I reluctantly decided to call a crusade. Knights from northern France moved south . . .'

'But I bet lots of crusaders were carried away by greed and love of fighting, as well as religious fanaticism,' broke in Maureen. 'I don't think you should have called it at all.'

'The Albigensian Crusade was absolutely appalling!' cried Christobel. 'Tens of thousands of people died. In one town alone, 7,000 people who had fled to a church for refuge were killed – Catholics and Cathars alike! There is a frightful quote attributed to the abbot of Citeaux: "Kill them all. God will know his own." It may be apocryphal, but it pretty well sums up the attitude of crusaders at the time.'

'Medieval statistics are notoriously unreliable,' commented Innocent/Wade, 'So it is impossible to know how many really died, but I deeply regret the undeniable fact that some knights *did* use excessive force. However, the most significant event of my pontificate was undoubtedly the Fourth Lateran Council in 1215. Among other things, the council decreed that every bishop should investigate possible heresies in his diocese at least once a year. Heretics were to be excommunicated, handed over to secular authorities for punishment, and their property confiscated. Secular authorities who neglected to do their duty were to be excommunicated too, along with anyone who sheltered or defended heretics. Excommunicated persons were to be deprived of the allegiance of their vassals, and the rights to elect to public office, make a will, inherit property, and so on. Anyone who died while excommunicated was to be denied a Christian burial, and clergy who disregarded these decrees were to be removed from office.'

'Appalling!' shuddered Christobel.

'On a more positive note,' added Wade, 'I did my best to raise the standards of Christian clergy and promote proper preaching. The papal Inquisition, as such, did not come into being until the pontificate of Gregory IX (1227–41). He appointed special inquisitors to search out heretics. They were to co-operate with local bishops but ultimately they were under the direct authority of the papacy. Gregory also condoned the execution of unrepentant heretics by secular authorities, something the Fourth Lateran Council had *not* done. Worst of all, Innocent IV allowed inquisitors to use torture to obtain confessions in 1252.'

'I couldn't fit my rack and pulley onto my motorbike,' said our inquisitor regretfully. 'But I did have a cigarette lighter somewhere . . . Oh, yes, here it is.'

'I have gone along with this charade for long enough,' shrieked Melinda. 'I refuse to be tortured!'

'You don't need to be,' said Ruth soothingly. 'You've already made your confession. And, while I can in no way justify Innocent IV's awful decision to give inquisitors coercive powers, I do suspect that the use of torture by the medieval Inquisition has been sensationalized. Inquisitors were supposed to be experts in theology and pastoral care, concerned above all to *convert* heretics, not punish them. Bernard Hamilton says in his book on the Inquisition that relatively few people were actually put to death ...'

'But power corrupts,' said Maureen darkly, 'and some fanatics went around torturing and killing any possible heretic they could get their hands on – with the support of the Church and the State. I read that in 1239 nearly 200 Cathars were burnt at the stake, and the King of Navarre and a whole lot of bishops were there to watch the show. A chronicler wrote that it was "a holocaust, very great and pleasing to God".'

'How could a Christian possibly think that?' exclaimed Kirsty, very much troubled.

'Christendom was a compulsory society,' explained Wade, 'and heresy was the equivalent of treason. Even Thomas Aquinas saw nothing wrong with killing heretics. He argued that if it was all right for the state to kill those who issued counterfeit coins on the grounds that they were enemies to the common good, the death penalty for heretics who corrupted the faith and endangered souls was even more justifiable.'

'I don't think that there should be capital punishment for any crime whatsoever,' maintained Christobel firmly.

Ruth said that she felt the same way. 'However,' she went on, 'the papal Inquisition was probably a more civilized form of repression of heresy than outbreaks of mob violence against religious non-conformers, which also took place in the medieval period. And the massacre of the Cathars in 1239 was an extraordinary event. The inquisitor who organized it was eventually deposed and imprisoned for life on account of his excesses.'

'And the ... er ... effectiveness of the Church's fight against heresy depended to a very great extent on the cooperation of secular authorities,' whispered Derek. 'That . . . er . . . varied considerably from area to area. And, as I think that I am supposed to be the . . . er . . . secular authority here, I demand that you release Melinda immediately, Jason.' Poor Derek. It's not easy to radiate an air of authority when you've lost your voice.

'I should also point out that it is not known what happened to Peter Waldo,' continued Derek valiantly. 'I don't think he was ever . . . er . . . convicted . . .'

'Spoil-sport,' sighed Jason. 'Well, that's all folks. The Inquisition's over.'

'But you haven't asked me who I am,' said Christobel in an aggrieved tone.

'Who are you?' we chorused.

'Joan of Arc!'

'I thought she was a saint, not a heretic,' said Maureen vaguely. 'She heard voices and dressed like a man.'

'She was a simple French peasant girl who received wonderful mystical visions,' gushed Christobel. 'She was also incredibly brave and led an amazing movement of popular resistance to the English troops who were overrunning France during the terribly tedious Hundred Years War. More than anyone else, Joan deserves credit for the French King's ultimate victory in the 1450s. Tragically, however, she was captured by the English in 1430. She was tried by an awfully biased bishop and an inquisitor, condemned as a witch, and burnt at the stake. It was frightfully unjust!'

'Her condemnation had very little to do with religion,' commented Wade, 'and a lot to do with politics. As far as the English were concerned, her death was a political necessity, and the Inquisition proved to be a convenient tool. The notorious Inquisition in Spain was also a political weapon in the hands of the monarchy . . .'

'However, in Joan's case the Inquisitor-General of France supervised a re-trial in 1455, which overturned her condemnation,' recounted Ruth.

'That was political too,' asserted Melinda. 'The King of France didn't want people to think that he owed his throne to a witch. All in all, I am forced to conclude that the Inquisition was one of the most disgusting aspects of the medieval Church.'

'And it was one which the Protestant reformers did *not* reject,' said Jason unkindly. 'They burnt heaps of people at the stake, too!'

'And we should not forget that torture is still used as a method of interrogation or a means of punishment in many countries in the world today,' remarked Wade soberly. 'In fact, I suspect that the use of torture in the twentieth century far exceeds that of the medieval period.'

This reminded Christobel that she had leaflets advertising a meeting of her social concerns group to hand out.

'I made a particular point of inviting Jason,' she told me afterwards, 'because he needs to discover that Christian churches are not inward-looking religious clubs but groups of people deeply committed to resolving the crises facing the world today. It is painfully obvious, to me at least, that someone like Jason is not going to be impressed by Bible-bashing, hyped-up Pentecostal rallies or free pizza. He needs to meet Christians whom he can actually RESPECT.'

I wished her luck.

WEEK·ELEVEN

St Francis of Assisi

'Right,' said Wade as soon as we were all seated, 'today we are going to look at Francis of Assisi, one of the most popular and influential Christians of all time. I want us to consider his historical context, what he actually did, and how his vision can be applied to the crises of post-modern culture. First: What was his historical context?'

'There was a great gulf between the higher clergy and the laity,' answered Melinda. 'The papacy was driven by political ambitions to dominate Europe. Monks were more interested in managing their estates than anything else. Lower clergy were poorly trained, with low moral standards, and church services and the Bible were in Latin, beyond the understanding of ordinary people. As a result, the so-called "Age of Faith" might be better described as an age of ignorance, heresy and sloth.'

'There was a lot of unnecessary legalism, as well,' declared Frank. 'Church councils and canon lawyers went on and on, trying to work out how many sacraments there were, and all kinds of rules and regulations, while people like the Waldensians who lived the simple life of the gospels were persecuted.'

'There was an increase in devotion to the humanity of Jesus, and desire for a personal relationship with him,' said

Ruth in a more positive tone. 'Wonder at his birth, suffering or death dominate poems and hymns like that attributed to St Bernard of Clairvaux:

O sacred Head, now wounded,
With grief and shame weighed down,
Now scornfully surrounded
With thorns, thine only crown!

By 1200 it was common to find crucifixes in churches, and devotion to the Virgin Mary also gained in prominence. The Ave Maria and the Rosary date from the twelfth century . . .'

'And pilgrimages and relics were still popular, too,' observed Melinda distastefully.

'So entrepreneurs cashed in on devotion to Jesus and Mary by selling drops of his sweat and her milk,' grinned Jason. 'Which, somehow or other, had been miraculously preserved for over a thousand years! Overall, saints from the very early Church seem to have become much more fashionable at this time than the hermits, monks and holy men from other ages. A French monastery had Mary Magdalene's arm, and when Hugh, Bishop of Lincoln, visited the abbey at the end of the twelfth century he chewed a bit of it off, which really upset the monks, but he replied that if he could touch the body of Christ in the mass, he could apply his teeth to Mary's bones!'

'Clear evidence that people were not taught the Bible, but assimilated all kinds of vulgar beliefs,' said Melinda, wrinkling her nose.

'Yes, but what about economic developments?' broke in Wade impatiently.

I remembered that Wade had said something in the tutorial on the twelfth-century Renaissance about an increase in population, towns and trade. Blurted that out.

'And what did that result in?' prompted Wade.

'Better living conditions,' pronounced Melinda.

'Freedom from feudal bonds, the rise of the universities, the birth of democracy . . .' cried Christobel, throwing her arms into the air and accidentally hitting Frank who was sitting beside her.

'CAPITALISM!' exploded Wade. 'The rise of the bourgeoisie. The exploitation of the working class. Inequality, suffering, poverty . . .'

'And the Church was ill-equipped to minister to the growing population of the towns,' added Ruth, 'as parishes and monasteries were geared to a predominantly rural society.'

'Exactly, and that, at last, brings us to Francis of Assisi,' said Wade with an exasperated sigh. 'Francis Bernadone was born in the Italian city of Assisi in about the year 1182. His father was a wealthy cloth merchant, so Francis enjoyed a privileged upbringing . . .'

'Sidney Painter says that he was "a gay young man who liked to sing the songs of courtly love and fight in the perpetual local wars between Assisi and her neighbours",' interrupted Maureen. 'Actually, several books I read said that he was "gay", but they were all published some time ago so I don't suppose they mean that he was homosexual. It's a pity that "gay" has got those connotations now because it used to be a really pretty girl's name. One of my cousins . . .'

'Francis became increasingly dissatisfied with his life and conscious of the poverty and suffering around him,' began Wade again.

'He reached a critical turning-point in his life when he forced himself to kiss a leper,' said Christobel in an awed voice. 'He later wrote that "the Lord granted me . . . to begin to do penance in this way, that, when I was in sin, it seemed to me very horrible to see lepers, and the Lord himself led me among them and I helped them. And when I left them that which had before seemed to me horrible was transformed into sweetness of body and soul." '

'And a crucifix above an altar in a little church outside Assisi spoke to him,' contributed Kirsty eagerly. 'It said: "Francis, go and repair my house, which you see is in ruins." '

'People reckon that that was the start of the Franciscan revival of the Church,' remarked Jason, 'but Francis himself took it literally and began to beg for stones. He also sold some of his father's cloth to get money to rebuild the church, which didn't please his father at all. He thought his son had gone mad, and demanded the money back. Francis retaliated by completely disowning his father. He stripped off all his clothes and flung them at his feet, in a public square in Assisi, crying: "Now I will say freely: 'Our Father who art in heaven, not father Peter Bernadone', for I now surrender to him not only his money, but all my clothes. Naked I will go to the Lord." Then not only his father but the whole town of Assisi must have thought that he was nuts.'

'Francis spent the following couple of years engaged in solitary prayer, caring for lepers and repairing churches,' lectured Wade. 'Eventually, in 1206, he discovered his vocation in life when heard Matthew 10:7–10 read in church.'

' "Preach saying, 'The kingdom of heaven is at hand.' Heal the sick, raise the dead, cleanse lepers, cast out demons. You received without pay, give without pay. Take no gold, nor silver, nor copper in your belts; no bag for your journey, nor two tunics, nor sandals, nor a staff," ' quoted Frank.

'Yes, we all know that,' glared Wade. 'According to Francis' earliest biographer, when he heard those verses Francis called out: "This is what I wish; this is what I am seeking", and he took off his shoes, put on a habit of rough material, and immediately began to preach the need for repentance. After a while, a man called Bernard from another wealthy family in Assisi decided to join him. Francis sought guidance from scripture on how to proceed and came across Matthew 19:21, the same verse that greatly inspired Peter Waldo ("If you would be perfect, go, sell your possessions and give to the poor."). Bernard consequently gave away his worldly goods, and others came and followed his example. When they reached eight in number Francis sent them out two by two to proclaim peace to men and repentance for the remission of sin. By 1209 there were twelve friars minor, or little brothers, as Francis called them, and they decided to go to Rome to ask for a blessing from Pope Innocent III. They won the Pope's approval, and within a few years there were thousands of Franciscan friars throughout Europe. So what did Francis achieve?'

'He realized the importance of the Bible and the need for evangelism,' replied Melinda, graciously giving praise where praise was due. 'He helped put Christ back into Christianity, and he paved the way for the Reformation by giving people the Word of God.'

'He was devoted to Jesus,' said Ruth quietly, 'and passionately committed to living as he had lived. Eventually he was honoured by miraculously receiving the stigmata, wounds in his hands and feet as if he had been crucified.'

'He also celebrated Christmas in a stable, which made people start to have nativity scenes,' said Kirsty.

'He was marvellously at one with nature,' enthused Christobel. 'I just adore his Canticle of Brother Sun, Sister Moon, Brother Wind, Sister Water . . .'

'Yes, yes,' said Wade impatiently. 'There are lots of attractive myths and stories about Francis preaching to birds and animals, and so on. But we must not make the mistake of sentimentalizing him, thinking of him as just a nature-loving mystic or pious do-gooder. HE WAS ONE OF THE MOST RADICAL MEN WHO EVER LIVED. At a time when the feudal nobility laid great stress on social status, Francis embraced the dregs of society and treated all his "brothers", whatever their backgrounds, as equals. At a time when capitalism was becoming a powerful force, Francis completely rejected the possession of material goods and lived a life of absolute poverty. (As an example of his utter contempt for wealth, when he discovered that one of his friars had a coin, he ordered the man to carry it in his mouth to a pile of dung.) At a time when the Church was dominated by a clerical hierarchy, Francis was a layman. At a time when universities were emerging as educational institutions and theology was becoming an academic discipline, Francis disdained knowledge and cleverness in favour of the profound wisdom of the Bible. At a time when monks lived in monasteries, shut away as much as possible from the outside world, Francis and his followers wandered throughout the world as homeless pilgrims, ministering wherever there was need. At a time when monks took vows of personal poverty, but many monasteries enjoyed corporate wealth, Francis insisted that his followers were to practise corporate poverty as well, even to the extent of having to beg for their daily food. Poverty, simplicity, humility, equality and fraternity were the values espoused by Francis, not greed, pride, power . . .'

'How come Francis got to be a saint, while Peter Waldo ended up a heretic?' said Frank.

'Although Francis was amazingly non-conformist, he paradoxically remained absolutely devoted to the Church,' explained Christobel. 'He once wrote: "If I were as wise as Solomon, and met the poorest priests of all the world, I would still refuse to preach against their will in the parish in which they live." And he particularly promised to obey the Pope.'

'But he combined humility and obedience with a knack for getting his own way,' said Ruth dryly. 'According to one story, a bishop refused to give him a licence to preach in his diocese. Francis bowed his head and withdrew, but soon came back again. The bishop asked: "What do you want, brother? What is it now?" St Francis replied: "My lord, if a father repulses his son through one door he must come back by another." The bishop was won over by his humility and gave him and his brothers a general licence to preach. On another occasion, Francis was invited to a dinner party hosted by Cardinal Hugolino, later Pope Gregory IX. As was his custom, he first went out begging, and then arrived late at the Cardinal's house and handed the stale scraps of food to the other guests. The Cardinal was, not unnaturally, rather offended at this, but after Francis privately gave him a homily on apostolic poverty, he responded: "My son, do what is good in your eyes, since God is with you, and you with him."'

'How does Francis challenge us today?' asked Wade with passionate fervour.

'He reminds us that we must take seriously the Word of God if we are to revive the Church,' declared Melinda. Frank agreed.

'He challenges us to live in an atmosphere of love for all God's children and God's creation, to recognize in all things the hand of the Creator,' cried Christobel.

'And to preserve the heart of the Gospel through loving service, to be totally committed to our Lord and the kingdom of God,' added Ruth.

'We live in a time of global crises: social, economic and ecological,' thundered Wade. 'There is appalling poverty in Third World countries, and increasing unemployment in the First World. Advances in science and technology have resulted in hundreds of thousands of jobs disappearing forever . . .'

'Clearly wages need to be lowered,' commented Melinda in an assured tone. 'A century ago thousands of people were employed as domestic servants, but now wages are too high and unions have secured totally unrealistic working conditions . . .'

'You are, of course, speaking as a potential employer, not a potential housemaid,' said Wade sarcastically. 'The result of lower wages, if you had your wish, would be to increase the gap between the "haves" and the "have nots", which is already wide enough as it is. You'd escalate suffering, social dislocation, crime and violence. In contrast, Francis responded to the needs of his day with love, compassion and kindness. He radically identified with the poor, and with the poor Christ. He showed that the Church should not be just doctrines and rites, but the children of God, committed to following Christ and loving and serving one another, especially those in greatest need.'

'And he actually seemed to enjoy being a poor, filthy beggar!' said Jason in an amazed tone. 'I think he was a fanatic, a real nut-case,' he added quickly, 'but you have to admire the way he lived out his convictions.' He shot Christobel a significant-looking glance. She turned away, rather peevishly.

'It's all very well to be idealistic,' interjected Melinda, smarting from Wade's implication that she didn't show love, compassion and kindness. 'But idealism without organization is bound to fail. Francis was a very poor organizer. He was more interested in doing things like dashing off to preach to the Muslims than governing his friars on a day-to-day basis. A rule was eventually drawn up for his thousands of followers, but organizational problems continued to beset the order. In particular, there were bitter disputes between those who wanted to live in simplicity and absolute poverty, and those who did not disdain a university education, some possessions and a house to live in. By the end of the thirteenth century the latter were in the majority. Moorman writes in his *History of the Franciscan Order* (p. 154):

> There was [henceforth] to be greater security and stability, greater privilege and prestige. The typical friar was to be no longer the wandering evangelist who worked in the fields, tended the sick, slept in barns and churches, a simple, devout, homely soul content to take the lowest place and be *idiota et subditus omnibus*, but a member of a religious house, well-educated and well-trained, a preacher and director of souls, a man whom the community could respect and whose services would be valued.

'The papacy strongly supported the moderate wing. During the early fourteenth century the hard-line "Spiritual" Franciscans were condemned as subversive and dangerous to the social order, and some were burnt at the stake as heretics. As with the monastic orders, the mendicant or begging orders swiftly declined. Thus Chaucer's friar in *The Canterbury Tales* is licentious, worldly and corrupt:

> He knew the taverns well in every town
> And every innkeeper and barmaid too
> Better than lepers, beggars and that crew,
> For in so eminent a man as he
> It was not fitting with the dignity
> Of his position, dealing with a scum
> Of wretched lepers; nothing good can come
> Of commerce with such slum-and-gutter dwellers,
> But only with the rich and victual-sellers.
> But anywhere a profit might accrue
> Courteous he was, and lowly of service too.

He was the finest beggar of his batch . . .
For though a widow mightn't have a shoe,
So pleasant was his holy how-d'ye-do
He got his farthing from her just the same.'

Melinda finished on a triumphant note and slapped her note-book shut.

'Chaucer's friar is a caricature,' said Wade crossly. 'Given the enormous number of friars in the late Middle Ages, it is not surprising that some were less than committed to Francis's original ideals. They also tended to arouse the jealousy and hostility of local clergy because they carried out much the same functions as parish priests, but they were free to move about. A lot of people probably preferred to confess their sins to wandering friars rather than local priests, and friars attracted alms that might otherwise have gone to priests. They were also not subject to bishops like the ordinary clergy, and so they contributed to the weakening of episcopal authority, and papal centralization in the late Middle Ages. However, the point that I want to make is that Francis's ideals are still very relevant TODAY. In Latin America liberation theologians . . .'

'And my point,' retorted Melinda, 'is that one has to be realistic! People today may be carried away by the ideals of so-called "liberation theology", but that is only thinly disguised Marxism, and, if it is allowed to go on unchecked, it will lead to political turmoil and violent conflict. Jesus did not instigate a political or an economic revolution. He said: "Give to Caesar what is Caesar's, and to God what is God's." I make no apology for being a law-abiding, hard-working citizen who enjoys a relatively comfortable lifestyle as a result. It is utterly ridiculous to suppose that we should all go to the extremes which Francis went to . . .'

'I think that we are . . . er . . . running out of time,' intervened Derek anxiously.

'Yes, and I must leave or I'll be late for an appointment with my financial advisor,' Melinda announced with a defiant toss of her head.

'How did your social concerns meeting go last night?' I asked Christobel on the way out.

'Victoria Marville-Jones gave the most moving account of suffering in the Third World that I have ever heard,' replied Christobel bitterly. 'We had the largest turn-out ever, and by the time she finished there was scarcely a dry eye in the audience.'

'What went wrong?' I inquired, for obviously something had.

'After telling us about the suffering millions, and beseeching us to give every penny that we possibly could to the collectors at the back of the hall (Barclaycard, Visa and American Express cards accepted), Victoria asked if anyone had any questions they would like to put to her.'

'Well?' I prompted.

'Jason', said Christobel in an ominous tone, 'asked if she was the owner of the almost brand new, top-of-the-range imported car which was parked at the front of the hall.'

Oh dear.

'She admitted that she was, so Jason helpfully suggested that she trade it in on a push-bike, and donate the left-over cash to the aforesaid suffering millions. Victoria replied that she would dearly like to do so, but she could hardly take her four little children to school each day on a push-bike, could she?

'Jason then asked which school had the honour of educating the little Marville-Joneses. Victoria declared, rather defensively, that they went to a *Christian* school. Jason said: "*Which* Christian school?" Eventually poor Victoria had to own up. It was, of course, one of the most exclusive and expensive, as everyone in the audience well knew. Victoria then angrily acknowledged that she came from a privileged background, and said that was why she put so much effort into fundraising – to do her bit to help those less well off.

'Jason then magnanimously agreed that she had chosen a very noble cause to work for, but, as a poor university student, he highly resented being exhorted to give away what little money he had by a professional fundraiser in a designer suit, with a luxury car parked outside, and kids whose pocket money probably exceeded his weekly income – their school fees certainly did. Victoria (almost in tears) maintained that she was following Christ as best she could, whereupon Jason said that he hadn't realized that Jesus had driven around Palestine in a leather-upholstered chariot. By this time, half the audience was in shock, the other half was tittering, and hardly anyone stayed for supper, so I've got a freezer full of cream cakes just when I am trying to lose weight!'

WEEK·TWELVE

Medieval women

'Who', asked Christobel, 'was St Francis of Assisi's most faithful follower?'

'St Clare,' replied Ruth promptly. She was right, at least as far as Christobel was concerned.

'Clare was born into an aristocratic family in Assisi,' went on Christobel, her eyes sparkling. 'She was very beautiful and could have made a brilliant marriage. However, in 1212 she was so inspired by Francis's preaching that she ran away from her family and dedicated her life to God. Francis cut her lovely hair and she took off her elegant gown and jewels and put on a dress of dreary grey sackcloth. She was only eighteen at the time and her family was absolutely furious, especially as her younger sister joined her. Francis placed them both in the little church of San Damiano outside Assisi, and Clare lived there in absolute poverty until her death in 1253. Moorman says that she "wore only the simplest and roughest of clothes, slept on the floor, and ate so little that it is hard to know how she lived at all". Other women joined her and they became known as the Poor Ladies. By the time Clare died there were fifty living at San Damiano, and twenty other convents of Poor Ladies had been established.'

'Why is it such a good thing to live in poverty?' asked Kirsty with a worried expression. I could guess what she was thinking. I'd find it pretty difficult to wear rough clothes, sleep on the floor and eat hardly anything, too.

'Above all, Clare sought to imitate our Lord,' explained Ruth. 'This comes out strongly in her letter to Agnes, the daughter of the King of Bohemia who wanted to follow her religious life. She exhorted Agnes to "look upon him who for you became the object of contempt, and follow him, making yourself contemptible for his sake in the world." She also believed that she was freed from the distractions of wealth and material possessions to love and pray. She completely surrendered herself to God and lived in absolute trust and dependence on him. Furthermore, she took seriously the promises of the Beatitudes, writing to Agnes that: "If you suffer with him, you shall reign with him; if you weep with him you shall rejoice with him; if you die with him on the cross of tribulation, you shall possess heavenly mansions . . ." '

'But you cannot earn your salvation,' said Melinda firmly. 'It is by faith alone.'

'It wasn't a case of earning salvation but using ascetical measures to foster spiritual progress,' replied Ruth. 'I wouldn't necessarily recommend such a life today, but in Clare's case it seemed to work. Despite her poverty she radiated peace and joy, and while she was very hard on herself, she was extremely kind and gentle to her sisters. She was a leader who never shrank from menial tasks, but seized every opportunity to serve others. Successive popes tried to moderate her lifestyle, but she remained committed to it and eventually won from Innocent IV the right to include the principle of communal (as well as personal) poverty in her monastic rule.'

'She was the friend of popes and cardinals,' exclaimed Christobel proudly. 'Gregory IX shared his problems with her and asked for her prayers, and Innocent IV rushed to her deathbed and wanted to canonize her on the spot, but was persuaded to follow customary procedure. An inquiry was made into her virtues and miracles, and two years after her death (which was incredibly soon by the standards of the Roman curia) Alexander IV presided at her canonization, declaring: "Her feet stood upon earth while her soul was already in heaven."'

'She kept a cat,' said Maureen. We all looked at her in surprise. 'I read about it in Joanne Turpin's book *Women in Church History: Twenty Stories for Twenty Centuries*. She had a hole cut in the refectory door so it could pop in and out for meals. I've been feeding a stray cat lately. I wasn't going to get another pet because they are such a bother when you go away, but this is a real friendly little thing and I've grown quite attached to it. I'm not going to give it its own cat door, though. It comes and sits on the window ledge whenever it wants to come in . . .'

'Did you . . . er . . . have anything else that you would like to say about St Clare, Christobel?' asked Derek.

'Only that I'm absolutely sure that Clare would have wanted to have joined Francis in active mission (preaching and helping the underprivileged) but Francis, usually so nonconformist, bowed to social prejudice and incarcerated her in a convent. However, at about the same time in the Low Countries and Germany an amazing movement was emerging which *did* allow religious women more freedom. The Beguines were not an appendix to a male movement, as was so often the case. They had no definite founder, no definite organization, and no common rule. They took no formal, irreversible vows, and some women stayed with their families while others lived in small groups . . .'

'I'm not sure how that would have worked,' interrupted Maureen. 'There's nothing like living with your friends for ruining friendship. When I went on a ten-day bus tour with Enid I got fed up with her always taking the window seat and talking at night when I wanted to go to sleep . . .'

'Of course, the Beguines were awfully saintly women,' said Christobel excusingly, 'and they usually lived in poverty and chastity and supported themselves by manual labour: working in hospitals, weaving, and so on. They also spent a lot of time praying and meditating, and some bishops and clergy realized that they were really holy and deserved support. However, other male chauvinist pigs declared that they should either marry or go into a proper nunnery. In 1312 the horrible Council of Vienne decreed that they were "afflicted by a kind of madness", and their way of life was to be "permanently forbidden and altogether excluded from the Church of God". They didn't totally die out, but they were gradually institutionalized – forced back into the traditional religious life for women.'

There was no mistaking the bitter tone in Christobel's voice, so I thought that it was rather rash of Jason to immediately assert that some medieval women were real nut-cases. 'A friar wrote a biography about someone called Christina in the thirteenth century,' he disclosed. 'According to this, Christina lived a devout, solitary life as a shepherdess until she was thirty-two. Then she died. However, she didn't stay dead but came back to life. After smelling the scent of heaven she couldn't bear the stink of ordinary humans so she ran into a forest to hide. Then she perched on the top of trees and church steeples. When she found that she couldn't live without food, God miraculously made milk come from her breasts. Then she thought that she had to go through purgatory while still on earth, so she threw herself into ovens and stood on revolving water mills in icy cold water. Her family got fed up with all this and tried to stop her by tying her to a tree.

After a while her buttocks began to fester and bleed from chaffing against the wood, so another miracle occurred: oil came from her breasts. She rubbed it on her bum and spread it on her bread.'

'Disgusting!' said Melinda.

'Not the kind of miracle you'd expect from an upper-middle-class Anglo-Saxon God,' agreed Jason cheerfully. 'Nevertheless, her family was so impressed that they released her and she floated about filled with the Holy Spirit until she finally died for good.'

'She was a wonderful mystic,' suggested Christobel, rather feebly.

'What exactly is a mystic?' inquired Kirsty, embarrassed at betraying her ignorance but wanting to know.

'Someone who experiences God in a special way,' answered Ruth gently.

'Someone whose knowledge of God transcends ordinary experience,' cried Christobel, 'transcends reason, transcends the ability of language to describe . . .'

'You mean it doesn't make sense,' said Jason.

'Yes. No!' responded Christobel confusingly. 'I mean, it may not seem to make sense to the non-mystic, but the mystic herself realizes that she has reached a deeper level of her soul than normal, that she has discovered a divine reality far more real than anything else. As a matter of fact, the greatest medieval English mystic was Julian of Norwich . . .'

'I thought we were supposed to be talking about medieval women,' remarked Frank.

'Julian *was* a woman,' retorted Christobel. 'Sadly, very little is known about her, but she spent a considerable part of her life as a recluse or anchoress. She lived in a little cell built onto St Julian's Church in Norwich, which is presumably how she got her name. On 8 May 1373, when she was seriously ill, she received the most marvellous visions and spiritual insights. She later meditated on her experiences and wrote down her wonderful discoveries about divine love and the female side of God.'

'Julian's theology has always appealed to me,' revealed Ruth. 'It is so warm and positive! She had a vivid revelation of our Lord's agony on the cross – and his joy in doing his Father's will and his great love for us. She saw that "God is everything which is good, and the goodness which everything has is God." Our Lord "is to us everything which is good and comforting for our help. He is our clothing, who wraps and enfolds us for love, embraces us and shelters us, surrounds us for his love, which is so tender that he may never desert us . . ." '

'And he is our true mother!' declared Christobel, picking up a copy of Sheila Upjohn's *In Search of Julian of Norwich*. She quoted Upjohn's translation of Julian's insights:

A kind loving mother, who knows and understands the needs of her child, looks after it tenderly as is her way and nature. And as it grows bigger she changes her ways, but not her love. And when it grows older still, she allows it to be punished, to break it from vice and lead it to goodness and grace. And our Lord does the same thing, truly and well, to those he brings up.

A mother may sometimes let her child fall and be unhappy in many ways for its own good. But she will never allow any real harm to come to the child, because of the love she bears it. And though an earthly mother may have to allow her child to die, our heavenly mother Jesus will not allow any one of us who is his child to perish. For his is all power, all wisdom, and all love, and no one is but he.

But often, when our falling and our miserable sin is shown to us, we are so ashamed that we scarcely know where to put ourselves. But our loving mother does not want us to run away

from him then, for he does not love us less. But he wills that we
behave as children do. For when they are unhappy or fright-
ened, they run quickly to their mother for help, with all their
might . . .'

'Some people think that Julian may have been a nun before
she became an anchoress, but I reckon that she must have
been a real mother,' put in Maureen. 'She could have gone off
to her cell after her husband and children died during a
plague – there were lots of plagues in the fourteenth century.
I wonder if she kept a cat? The thirteenth-century *Ancrene
Riwle*, or *Anchoresses' Rule Book*, says that anchoresses
should not keep any animals except a cat.'

'What did anchoresses actually do?' asked Kirsty.

'They got walled up in cells,' said Jason with morbid relish.
'And they had to stay in them for the rest of their lives. The
Saxon abbess Hrotsvit of Gandersheim wrote a play about a
prostitute, Thais, who was converted by her hermit uncle,
Paphnutius, who wanted to lock her up in a cell. Part of it is
quoted in *Peaceweavers: Medieval Religious Women* (Vol. 2,
p. 75):

Thais: My vileness does not refuse to go at once where your
paternity commands; but there is a certain inconvenience in
this dwelling which is difficult for my weakness to bear.

Paph: Now, what is this inconvenience?

Thais: I blush to say.

Paph: Come now, don't blush. Be thoroughly honest.

Thais: What is more inconvenient, or what could be more
disagreeable than having, in one and the same place, to
attend to the different needs of nature? Indeed, it would
soon become uninhabitable because of the excessive
stench.

Paph: Fear the cruelty of everlasting hell, and cease to shudder at things which pass away.

Thais: My weakness drives me into terror.

Paph: It is only right that you expiate the sweetness of the plea-
sure of evil delights by the vexation of excessive stench . . .'

'How awful,' said Kirsty, shocked again.

'Yes, well, Hrotsvit wrote in the tenth century,' responded
Christobel uneasily. 'I am sure that by Julian's time more
attention was paid to cleanliness and sanitation. We know
that she had a servant to look after her physical needs because
someone left a bequest to them both.'

'Nevertheless, an anchoress's life was quite unbiblical,'
interjected Melinda. 'We are supposed to live good Christian
lives in society, not run away from human contact through a
selfish desire to get special knowledge of God . . .'

'Or because of a totally wrong idea that we can earn our
salvation,' added Frank.

'But anchoresses did not turn their backs on humanity,'
objected Christobel. 'They prayed for the people in the town
or village where they lived. They counselled people who
came to them for spiritual guidance. They even acted as
mediators in all kinds of disputes. Some gained reputations as
healers or prophets . . .'

Ruth agreed. 'They might not have been actively engaged
in helping alleviate human suffering through charitable
endeavours,' she said, 'but they did help meet people's spiritual hunger, and that surely was a great service. And because
they were detached from the world and spent a great deal of
time in contemplative prayer, their ministry was probably
more effective than if they had remained in the world.'

'Well, you have to either admire their faith or conclude that
they were mad,' commented Wade.

'Definitely mad,' said Jason provocatively.

'Misguided,' corrected Melinda.

I seized the opportunity to make a contribution. 'According to the *Ancrene Riwle*, anchoress's cells usually had three windows.'

'What were they for?' asked Derek encouragingly.

'One opened into the church, so that the anchoress could take part in the mass. Another opened into a servant's room, so that the servant could pass through food and clean clothes, and the third opened onto the street so that people could talk to the anchoress.'

'We know that Marjorie Kempe visited Julian of Norwich and talked to her for some time,' said Wade. 'Marjorie was another mystic, although she is not as highly regarded as Julian.'

'She definitely was married,' affirmed Maureen. 'She had the sense to leave her husband, too. She went on lots of pilgrimages all over Europe and the Holy Land. But she had a peculiar spiritual gift. Whenever she thought about Christ's suffering and death (which was often), she burst into uncontrollable, hysterical tears. She drove everyone unfortunate enough to be travelling with her up the wall, so they tried to lose her whenever they could, or change ships when they saw her coming! As I know full well, there's nothing worse than spending a fortune on a holiday and then being stuck on a tour with someone you can't stand. It ruins your holiday.'

This prompted Christobel to inquire whether Maureen was still planning to go to France later this year. 'It's funny that you should ask,' replied Maureen, 'because I had to decide last Friday whether I'd go or not. It was tempting, but I can't really afford to go away just now and I want to be available to help my daughter Gail with the new baby. How do you like my hair?'

I had been thinking all through the tutorial that Maureen looked somehow different, but I hadn't been able to work out why. Realized now that her hair was a bit darker and curlier. We all agreed that her new hairstyle suited her, and Maureen looked modestly pleased. She then revealed that she's been invited to dinner next Saturday night, followed by ballroom dancing. One of her friends goes dancing with her husband every week, and she's found an obliging widower to escort Maureen. We should not, Maureen hastened to add, think that she was interested in romance (she's still completely off men) but she's sick of spending Saturday nights with only the television, lolly jar, cat and parrot for company.

After we had all wished Maureen well, Christobel announced that she had made a major, life-changing decision. 'On the one hand, it was absolutely thrilling reading about wonderful medieval women like Julian and Clare, but then I started to review my own life. They gave up so much for Christ. What have I done? So I decided . . .'

Surely Christobel wasn't going to dress in rags and lock herself in a cell? Couldn't somehow visualize it . . .

'So I decided to put my television set in the garage!' Tried to look suitably impressed.

'Yes, no more soap operas, no more commercials exhorting me to buy hedonistic goods that I do not really need. I am going to devote my evenings to reading classics of spirituality and practising contemplative prayer . . . that is, when I don't have to go to meetings, choir practice, and such like.'

'There are some really good things on the radio,' volunteered Maureen. 'I discovered that when my telly broke down last year. Some of them are quite religious, too.'

'Er . . . as usual we have run out of time,' intervened Derek. 'Much, much more could be said about medieval women, but I think that we have at least come to realize that they played a very significant, varied and . . . er . . . controversial role in the Church, and they can still challenge and inspire us today.'

Even Jason and Frank agreed.

WEEK·THIRTEEN

The late-medieval papacy

'Er . . . perhaps we should start with Pope Boniface VIII,' began Derek. 'He was elected in 1294 and died in 1303. What is he most . . . er . . . famous for?'

'Being arrogant, rude, pompous and intolerant,' replied Melinda firmly. 'In 1302 he promulgated the outrageous bull *Unam Sanctam*: "Therefore we declare, state, define and pronounce that it is altogether necessary to salvation for every human creature to be subject to the Roman Pontiff."'

'Bull's the word for it,' muttered Frank.

'*Unam Sanctam* really pissed off the French king, Philip IV,' said Jason. 'At a royal council in 1303 Boniface was accused of heresy and other crimes. I like the other crimes best:

He was not ashamed to declare that he would rather be a dog or an ass or any brute animal than a Frenchman . . . He is reported to say that fornication is not a sin any more than rubbing the hands together is . . . He has often said that he would ruin himself and the whole world and the whole Church to lay low the king and the French people . . . He has had silver images of himself erected in churches to perpetuate his damnable memory, so leading men into idolatry . . . He has a private demon whose advice he takes in all matters . . . He is guilty of the crime of sodomy . . . He has caused many clerics to be murdered in his presence, rejoicing in their deaths . . . He does not fast on fast days . . . He is publicly accused of treating inhumanly his predecessor Celestine . . . imprisoning him in a dungeon and causing him to die there swiftly and secretly . . .'

'Did he really have people murdered?' said Kirsty, looking shocked.

'The charges, if based on any fact at all, were doubtless greatly exaggerated,' responded Wade. 'For instance, his outburst (probably genuine) that he'd rather be a dog than French was cited as evidence for heresy: that he had implied that the French did not have immortal souls. Likewise, rumours abounded about the fate of Celestine. Celestine resigned, which triggered a lot of debate about whether it was possible for a pope to resign or not. Boniface, one of the foremost canon lawyers of the day, advised him that it was OK, and when Boniface was subsequently elected pope his enemies accused him of pressuring Celestine.'

'Celestine was a saintly, eighty-five-year-old hermit,' explained Derek. 'He never wanted to be pope, but was eventually elected because the cardinals hadn't been able to agree on anyone else for two years. Most historians accept that he . . . er . . . voluntarily resigned, but he was very popular and rather . . . er . . . gullible. Boniface was apparently afraid that he would become a pawn in the hands of his opponents, and so he was confined to the castle of Fumone. There is no evidence that he was treated harshly, and he probably died of natural causes. He was, after all, very old.'

'And if he was a hermit, he probably liked being locked up,' concluded Jason cheerfully.

'That still doesn't excuse Boniface's arrogance,' retorted Melinda. 'His relatives fared much better than his opponents. He followed a policy of flagrant nepotism.'

'What issues lay behind the dispute between the Pope and the King of France?' asked Derek.

'The rise of the nation-states,' declared Wade. 'Everywhere in Europe in the late Middle Ages rulers strove to limit the power and independence of the Church within their territories. This naturally put them on a collision course with the papacy, which was striving to assert its universal lordship.'

'But what particularly led to the Boniface–Philip dispute was the fact that the kings of France and England were forever at war against one other,' announced Christobel. 'Both tried to raise money for their awful military campaigns by taxing the clergy. However, the Fourth Lateran Council had decreed in 1215 that kings could only tax clergy with the Pope's consent, and in 1296 Boniface threatened anyone who demanded or paid such tax with excommunication. Philip was really frightfully clever and retaliated by simply banning the export of all gold and silver from France. Since a large portion of Boniface's income came from France, he was eventually so financially pressed that he had to give in. He acknowledged that kings could tax clergy without papal permission in an emergency – and they got to define what an emergency actually was!'

'Philip clearly had an easy victory,' observed Wade, 'and he followed it up in 1301 by ordering the arrest and trial of a bishop on charges of simony, heresy and treason.'

'Was he guilty?' asked Kirsty, wide-eyed.

'It didn't matter whether he was guilty or not,' said Wade. 'As far as Boniface was concerned, the principle at stake was the right of the Pope alone to judge bishops. He demanded the release of the bishop, and ordered all the other French bishops to come to Rome for a synod. Philip told them to stay home. Less than half went. This, then, was the context in which *Unam Sanctam* was promulgated. Far from representing the peak of papal authority (as might seem to be the case), it was a desperate, defensive measure – an attempt to remind recalcitrant bishops that "there is one holy, Catholic and apostolic Church", and the Pope is its head.'

'Why didn't the Pope send his army into France?' demanded Maureen. 'He had one, didn't he?'

'The papal army could barely control the papal state, let alone invade another country,' said Jason scornfully. 'In fact, the reverse happened. Philip sent a troop of soldiers to Italy which nearly succeeded in kidnapping the Pope and bringing him back to France to stand trial for his supposed crimes.'

'I read that Boniface was really noble and brave,' put in Kirsty in an eager tone. 'When the soldiers broke into the palace where he was staying and stole all his gold, silver and clothes, he just said: "The Lord gave and the Lord taketh away . . ." '

'He was rescued by the local citizens,' went on Ruth, 'but he died a few weeks later, reportedly "broken in body and spirit".'

'The real significance of the Boniface–Philip dispute is the fact that it stimulated the growth of political thought,' said Wade briskly. 'Scholars like Giles of Rome looked for arguments to defend papal supremacy: for example, souls are governed by the Pope, bodies are governed by souls, temporal possessions exist to serve the needs of bodies, therefore all temporal things ultimately belong to the Pope.'

'But Jesus said that his kingdom is not of this world (John 18:36),' pointed out Frank. 'And although he was God, "he did not consider equality with God something to be grasped, but made himself nothing, taking the very nature of a servant" (Philippians 2:6–7). And it says in Romans 13:1 that "everyone must submit himself to the governing authorities . . ." '

'Yes, yes, those scripture passages were quoted by royalists in their defence of royal supremacy,' said Wade curtly. 'Pierre Dubois even went as far as declaring that the French king should take over all the temporal possessions and power of the Roman Church, give the Pope a pension in return, and force him to live in France!'

'That virtually did happen,' interjected Melinda. 'Clement V, a Frenchman, settled in Avignon in 1309, where the papacy remained for almost seventy years, totally dominated by France. All seven Avignon popes were French, as were 111 of the 134 cardinals they appointed, and they supported France during the Hundred Years War against England. It is hardly surprising that this disgraceful period has gone down in history as "the Babylonian captivity of the papacy".'

'Before he became pope Clement V was technically a subject of the English king,' remarked Ruth, 'and Avignon was not then part of France. It is true that French influence was strong, but the papacy was never as dependent on the French king as Pierre Dubois would have liked. Actually, the decision to move to Avignon was a very sensible one. Avignon was far more politically stable than Rome, and much more accessible to most people in western Europe.'

'The popes lived in decadent luxury, and nepotism was rife,' sniffed Melinda.

'I read about them in the *Oxford Dictionary of Popes* by J. Kelly,' said Maureen, suddenly entering the discussion, 'I'll read you what I jotted down. Clement V (1305–14) gave heaps of money and powerful positions to his family (that's what nepotism means, doesn't it?) but he was intelligent, devout and kindly. John XXII (1316–34) was old and feeble in health when he became pope, but he was very energetic and a real good administrator. He was also very pro his relatives and pro-France, but he lived extremely frugally and promoted missions in Asia. Benedict XII (1334–42) was of humble birth

(French, but humble). He was a "deeply learned theologian" and real keen to stamp out abuses in the Church. He got particularly stuck into drawing up strict new regulations for monks and friars. Kelly says that he was "just but hard and legalistic". Clement VI (1342–52) was much more easygoing. He had a luxurious court, put on great banquets and was a very generous patron of the arts. There were rumours about sexual misconduct, but Kelly concludes that he was "personally devout, a protector of the poor and needy who showed charity and courage when the Black Death appeared at Avignon in 1348–9, and defended the Jews when they were blamed for it". Wasn't that nice?'

Christobel agreed that it was.

'Where was I?' continued Maureen. 'Oh, yes, Innocent VI (1352–62) tried to reform the papal curia and eradicate abuses. He wanted to return to Rome, too, but he first had to get back control of the papal state which was overrun by petty tyrants, whatever that means. When he died "he had had his fill of anxieties and blighted hopes", poor man. Urban V (1362–70) was "austere, deeply religious, unworldly". Even when he became pope he lived like a Benedictine monk, praying and studying as well as administering whatever the Pope has to administer. He carried on with Innocent's reforms, reduced the luxury of the papal court, supported hundreds of poor students, and did lots of other good things. He managed to get back to Rome for a while, but it was so disease-ridden, dilapidated and politically unstable that he moved back to Avignon. Gregory XI (1370–77) was "deeply religious, with a strong mystical bent". He also went back to Rome, which was a real mistake because he got sick and died there.'

'He returned to Rome at the insistence of St Catherine of Siena,' exclaimed Christobel. 'She was an absolutely marvellous mystic, prophet, healer and peacemaker. She was the youngest of twenty-five children. She took a vow of virginity when she was only seven years old . . .'

'Can you blame her?' said Maureen, horrified. 'My daughter Gail is having enough trouble having one baby! Twenty-five would be a nightmare!'

'Perhaps some of the children died during the plague,' said Kirsty hopefully.

'Lots of people did die when the plague struck Siena,' revealed Christobel, 'and Catherine was absolutely wonderful. She helped the poor and afflicted as much as she possibly could. She also played a frightfully important role as a mediator between the Italian city-states which were forever at war against each other in the Middle Ages. But to get back to the point I wanted to make, she was firmly convinced that the Pope should be based in Rome, and she went to Avignon to tell Gregory XI so. She was awfully brave and frank when she met him: "To the glory of Almighty God I am bound to say that I smelled the stink of the sins which flourish in the papal court while I was still at home in my own town more sharply than those who have practised them, and do practise them, every day here."'

'She practically hounded the poor man back to Rome,' observed Ruth, 'where, as Maureen said, he died.'

'So the cardinals got together in the Vatican to elect a successor,' said Jason with relish. 'An unruly Roman mob was shrieking in the streets, demanding a Roman pope (or, at the very least, an Italian one). The cardinals wanted to get out of Rome alive, so they chose an Italian archbishop, who became known as Urban VI. He seemed like a good choice, because he was an experienced lawyer and administrator, but the cardinals soon discovered that they had made a big, big mistake. He was so rude and arrogant that he made Boniface VIII look like a model of humility, and he made it clear that he intended to reduce the cardinals' power. Most of them (the French lot) withdrew from Rome and, when they were safely away, declared that Urban's election was invalid because they had been subjected to too much pressure by the nasty Romans. They then elected another pope, Clement VII, who, by an amazing coincidence, happened to be a cousin of the French king. He settled down in Avignon, supported by France, Scotland and Spain. Urban stayed in Rome, appointed another lot of cardinals, and got the support of England, Germany and most of Italy. Both popes claimed to be the true pope and excommunicated each other. So much for the "one holy, Catholic and apostolic Church"!'

'What were the consequences of the schism?' asked Derek.

'It clearly showed the extent to which the papacy had declined,' proclaimed Melinda, 'and it provoked a growing number of people to reject the corrupt Church hierarchy and turn back to the Bible, which alone is infallible.'

'It forced people to reflect on the nature of the Church,' asserted Wade, 'although this had, of course, been going on for some time. John of Paris was one of the more moderate voices in the fall-out of the Boniface–Philip dispute in the early fourteenth century. He regarded spiritual and temporal authorities as distinct powers, neither intrinsically subordinate to the other. However, he did challenge the traditional view that the Pope can be judged by no one but God. He argued that the Pope is the steward of the goods of the Church and the defender of the faith rather than the supreme ruler of the Church. If he proves to be corrupt or heretical he should be deposed by a general council of the cardinals, acting on behalf of the whole Church. Marsilius of Padua went further in identifying "the people" as the ultimate source of all worldly authority. Legitimate power (political and ecclesiastical) exists, by the grace of God, through the will and consent of the people. In other words, it flows from the members of the Church or State to the head, rather than from the head (pope or king) down.'

'Such ideas did gain some support in the fourteenth century, but they were by no means popular or . . . er . . . universal,' said Derek.

'Unfortunately, when Urban VI and Clement VII died, successors were appointed in Rome and Avignon,' disclosed Ruth, 'and the schism looked like going on indefinitely. Scholars throughout Europe tried to work out a solution, especially, I think, at the University of Paris. Ideally, it would have been best if one or both of the popes had resigned, but neither would agree to. Eventually, in 1409, disillusioned cardinals from both sides held a council in Pisa. They formally deposed both popes and elected another – but neither the Roman nor the Avigonese pope would accept his deposition, so the Church was left with THREE popes.'

'Two was bad enough, three must have been an absolute disaster!' remarked Maureen.

'As far as I am concerned, one was too many,' muttered Frank.

'And so the Council of Pisa galvinized people who had been lukewarm about conciliarism into action,' swept on Wade.

'Conciliarism is the theory that power is . . . er . . . ultimately located not in a papal monarch, but in the Church itself, as represented in a general council,' Derek whispered to Kirsty who was looking confused.

'And in a rare display of unity, religious and secular leaders throughout Europe withdrew support from the three popes,' continued Wade, 'and flocked to the Council of Constance in 1414 . . .'

'The council went on for several years,' interrupted Jason, 'and someone reckoned that 72,400 people visited Constance during that time, including two popes, five patriarchs, the King of the Romans, representatives of eighty-three kings of Europe, Africa and Asia, 5,300 priests and scholars, 1,700 trumpeters and musicians, 1,400 merchants and innkeepers, and 700 prostitutes. It must have been quite a busy place!'

'One of the council's first decrees was *Sacrosancta*,' revealed Derek:

> This holy Council of Constance . . . declares, first, that it is lawfully assembled in the Holy Spirit, that it constitutes a General Council, representing the Catholic Church, and that therefore it has its authority immediately from Christ; and that all men, of every rank and condition, including the pope himself, are bound to obey it in matters concerning the Faith, the abolition of the schism, and the reformation of the Church of God . . .

'The English political historian John Figgis said that this is . . . er . . . "probably the most revolutionary official document in the history of the world",' went on Derek. 'Do you agree?'

'Well, the Council of Constance certainly ended the schism,' admitted Maureen. 'The Pisan pope was deposed, the Roman one resigned, and, although the Avignon one refused to go, I don't think that anyone took any notice of him any more. But I wouldn't exactly call the council revolutionary. It made Martin V pope, and he seemed to quickly reassert papal authority.'

'That's an interesting point,' said Derek. 'Why did the conciliar movement, after expressing its . . . er . . . authority so clearly in *Sacrosancta*, fade away so quickly?'

'I suspect that many of the people who took part in the council were more conservative than they have often been portrayed,' reflected Ruth. 'They wanted to restore papal government, not tear it apart. They only resorted to a council when all other means of resolving the schism failed.'

'Above all, the secular rulers who sent their representatives to Constance wanted the schism ended,' declared Wade, 'but it was obviously not in their best interests to promote a democratic reform of the Church which could be extended to the State. So long as the Pope didn't directly challenge their control of their national churches (as Boniface VIII had done), they were happy to maintain the status quo.'

'And the conciliar movement broke into lots of factions,' added Maureen. 'That's the problem with democracy: very good in theory, but easily stuffed up.'

'And so the Church missed an opportunity for carrying out real reforms,' stated Melinda.

'And getting rid of the papacy altogether,' added Frank gloomily.

As we were leaving I asked Maureen if she had had an enjoyable evening last Saturday. 'It was much better than I thought it would be,' she replied in a less-than-enthusiastic tone. 'I was a bit worried about going on a blind date, but Barry turned out to be real nice. He drove me home and I was just about to ask him in for a cup of tea when what do you think I saw?'

Couldn't guess. 'My ex-husband, sitting on the doorstep! I was real mad. It ruined my evening. His girlfriend has left him, so he thinks that he can come crawling back to me – physically, emotionally and financially bankrupt. That's what happens when you run off with someone half your age,' she added with rather vicious satisfaction.

'There is no hope of a reconciliation?' asked Ruth sympathetically.

'Would you want someone back who was physically, emotionally and financially bankrupt?' demanded Maureen. 'I gave him a piece of my mind and he went off, but I was so upset that I had to ask Barry to leave, too. Anyway, next day my daughter Gail came around, and, you know, with the baby due any minute now she's in a pretty vulnerable state. She cried and cried and said how awful it will be at the christening with the grandparents sniping at each other, and so on. Eventually she wore me down and I said I'd go with Don to see a marriage guidance counsellor, just to please her. But I really agree with that John-person who reckoned that corrupt popes should be deposed. The same should apply to husbands!'

Week·Fourteen
John Wycliffe

Melinda arrived looking cool and confident – not the slightest bit nervous at having to lead her first tutorial. Maureen, however, came in a few minutes later, flushed with excitement. Gail had been rushed to hospital! The baby was on its way! Richard, her son-in-law, had promised to ring as soon as he had news. Maureen reverently put down on the table in front of us her latest acquisition: a mobile telephone. Melinda lost some of her poise.

'We are here today to consider the life of one of the greatest English reformers,' she announced, abruptly cutting short Christobel's inquiries into the duration of Gail's contractions. 'I am very proud to say that English Protestants can look further back than Luther for the beginning of the English Reformation. There is much that could be said about John Wycliffe, but, as time is limited, I will confine myself to his teaching on the Bible, the Church, and the Eucharist. I will then consider his influence on the Czech reformer, John Hus.'

Melinda cleared her throat and checked her notes. 'I think that it is most appropriate that we start with the Bible. Wycliffe stoutly defended the divine authorship and inerrancy of the Bible. All truth is contained within it. It should be the supreme authority for all Christians. Everyone should be able to read it and understand it. Accordingly, Wycliffe inspired and initiated the translation of the Bible into English, thus setting into motion a process which ultimately resulted in the King James and Revised Standard Versions. Wycliffe was, needless to say, strongly opposed by the Church hierarchy who claimed that only priests were qualified to read and understand scripture. It was rightly feared that if the laity were able to compare the teaching of the Bible with the preaching and conduct of the clergy, the people would no longer respect . . .'

Maureen's phone rang. 'Boy or girl?' shrieked Maureen. 'What? . . . No, this is not Dial-a-Pizza. It's a medieval church history tutorial!' She put down the phone in disgust.

'Wycliffe's teaching on the Church proceeded naturally from his teaching on the Bible,' continued Melinda curtly. 'He set the authority of the Bible above the authority of the Church hierarchy. Decrees of popes and church councils are only valid if they are in accordance with scripture . . .'

Maureen's phone rang again. 'Hallo. Who is it? . . . What? . . . No, you cannot order this week's special. We're closed!' She slammed down the phone. 'Another wrong number! Two in two minutes is ridiculous.'

'Perhaps you have been given the pizza number by mistake,' suggested Kirsty.

'That'd be my luck!' said Maureen crossly. 'Some inconsiderate person will be hogging the line wanting to order his lunch just when Richard is trying to contact me to tell me that I'm a grandmother.' Melinda looked alarmed at the prospect of further interruptions to her tutorial.

'Didn't Wycliffe only completely reject the Church hierarchy after the Great Schism broke out?' asked Ruth.

'Naturally, that confirmed his belief that the hierarchy was at best unnecessary, and at worst the work of the Antichrist,' answered Melinda. 'After all, there is no mention of popes and cardinals in the Bible, and Wycliffe knew enough church history to realize that it was highly unlikely that Peter was ever the Bishop of Rome, and Rome had not occupied a position of supremacy in the very early Church. Instead, Wycliffe realized that the true Church is the invisible congregation of the elect, those predestined to salvation. He respected true ministers of the Word, but recognized that religious orders were sects which placed monastic rules above the Bible and encouraged monks and friars to think that they were superior to ordinary Christians and could earn their way to heaven. He also strongly disapproved of over-elaborate church buildings, gaudy decorations, unnecessary rituals and other unbiblical practices which distract people's attention from the worship of God. Sound preaching is more important than sacraments.'

'But he admitted that images in churches, prayers to saints, and that kind of thing could be aids to devotion,' protested Christobel. 'He really only attacked their misuse.'

'Nevertheless, he clearly regarded transubstantiation as thoroughly abhorrent,' maintained Melinda, 'and, in that respect, he went further than Martin Luther in dissociating himself from the medieval Church.'

'What actually is trans . . . um . . . you know?' asked Kirsty shyly.

'Er . . . the doctrine (defined at the Fourth Lateran Council in 1215) that the bread and the wine become the body and blood of Christ during mass,' responded Derek. 'The . . . er . . . outward appearance of the bread and wine remain, but the substance changes.'

'And Wycliffe thought that nothing was more horrible than the claim that the priest celebrating mass could actually create the body of Christ,' pronounced Melinda. 'It is contrary to scripture, early Church tradition and plain common sense. It is clearly promoted by the Catholic Church to bolster the authority of priests who alone can perform this false miracle, and it encourages the laity to worship the bread and wine as God, which is idolatrous . . .'

'But Wycliffe didn't deny the Real Presence,' pointed out Ruth. 'He accepted that our Lord is somehow present in the Eucharist . . .'

The phone rang again. 'Hallo. Who is it?' said Maureen suspiciously. 'Oh, Enid, it's you . . . Yes, I've got my new phone. Isn't modern technology amazing? . . . No, I didn't know that Jean couldn't play bowls this week, but I heard the other day that her leg was playing up again so I'm not surprised . . .' Melinda strummed her fingers on the table. 'Look, Enid, I've got to go now,' said Maureen hastily. 'I'm in the middle of a John Wycliffe tutorial . . . No, he isn't my tutor. He was someone in the Middle Ages who went on about the Bible a lot,' she explained, rather vaguely.

'Perhaps it would be helpful if we just . . . er . . . clarified who John Wycliffe actually was,' said Derek, when Maureen had finished her conversation.

'I thought that that would have been clear already,' declared Melinda impatiently. 'However, for those of you who may be having trouble grasping his significance, I will read the closing words in Edwin Robertson's *John Wycliffe: Morning Star of the Reformation*:

> He was upright, unafraid, persistent in the service of his Lord, a man who feared God and after that had no one else to fear.
>
> The memory of such a man, which his contemporaries tried to erase from the nation's mind, has stiffened the resolve of this country in many times of distress. And we live in such a time. His memory and his example should enable us to face better the challenges of the eighties and nineties.

Ours are not the problems that Wycliffe faced, but his total trust in the message of the Bible as clearly applying to his day and to any day, his firm determination that every person should have direct access to the fountain of faith, his impatience with all kinds of cant, pretence, hypocrisy and unmerited privilege, his honesty and integrity, are qualities we shall need. He would not have wanted to be canonized, but he was the kind of saint he looked for and we need.'

Silence.

'I read that he was born in about 1330 in Yorkshire,' ventured Kirsty at last, 'and he spent most of his life at Oxford University as a scholar, philosopher and theologian.'

'He has certainly been seen as a great reformer, a man of courage and integrity,' admitted Jason. Melinda looked pleased.

'But', continued Jason provocatively, 'he has also been described as a bad-tempered, extremely stubborn old academic, who was disillusioned and bitter as a result of failing to get promotion in the Church.'

'That is one explanation for why he criticized the Church,' said Derek. 'Can you ... er ... think of any others?'

'The Church was clearly corrupt!' burst out Melinda. 'You only have to read Chaucer's *Canterbury Tales* to appreciate that! Significantly, the *Canterbury Tales* was written just after Wycliffe died and a number of characters highlight abuses in the Church. The monk and nun are worldly, wealthy and lax, and the friar is licentious and immoral. The summoner, responsible for summoning people to the ecclesiastical courts, cheerfully accepts bribes, while the most repulsive of all characters, the pardoner, travels around selling "pardons" for sin to ignorant, superstitious people.'

'But wasn't Chaucer's parson really good?' inquired Kirsty. 'I copied this down:

A holy-minded man of good renown
There was, and poor, the Parson to a town,
Yet he was rich in holy thought and work.
He also was a learned man . . .
Who truly knew Christ's Gospel and would preach it
Devoutly to parishioners, and teach it . . .
Wide was his parish, with houses far asunder,
Yet he neglected not in rain or thunder,
In sickness or in grief, to pay a call
On the remotest, whether great or small . . .

'There's a lot more', added Kirsty, 'about how he not only taught the Bible but actually lived it.'

'He was clearly a Lollard,' said Melinda. 'The Lollards were adherents of Wycliffe's teaching. In contrast to the wealthy, lax and/or illiterate clergy, Lollards were nearly always poor, devout, educated men who preached the Bible. It is a tragedy that they were cruelly suppressed in the fifteenth century . . .'

'Of course, I was in labour for nearly two days when I had my first,' remarked Maureen suddenly. 'But with the second I barely had time to get to the hospital.'

'We must appreciate Wycliffe's context,' intervened Wade forcefully. 'The fourteenth century was a time of almost continual crisis in England. There was a series of natural disasters culminating in the Black Death in 1349. Estimates of the number of people who perished vary, but probably between one-third and one-half of the population died. A number of other outbreaks of plague followed in the late fourteenth and early fifteenth centuries. Not surprisingly, this led to great social dislocation. The feudal system had begun to break down well before 1349, but the plague hastened its demise. There were severe labour shortages, a great deal of land was left untended, food production fell and prices rose dramatically. Wages, however, were controlled by the infamous Statute of Labourers. In addition, heavy taxation was required to maintain the war against France. By the 1370s there were plenty of hungry, poor men and women who were disillusioned with what appeared to be a wealthy Church and an oppressive government, whose senior officials were, in many cases, clerics (the Chancellor, at one stage, was also the Bishop of Winchester). Anti-clericalism and economic and social grievances boiled over in the great Peasants' Revolt of 1381, in which the Lollards were implicated . . .'

'Wycliffe never approved of violent rebellion,' asserted Melinda.

'But he did argue that true lordship (secular and ecclesiastical) comes from God, and is held righteously only so long as the holder remains in a state of grace,' commented Ruth. 'Hence, he maintained that an unworthy priest should be deprived of his lordship. Surely the same argument could be applied to secular lords?'

'Well,' remarked Frank, 'the Bible does say that secular authorities exist by the will of God, and the first disciples were poor fishermen, and so on. Wycliffe reckoned that the main cause of problems in the Church was too much wealth and power, and so secular lords would be doing God's will if they took it away.'

'Wycliffe's teaching on lordship was condemned by Gregory XI in . . . er . . . 1377,' intervened Derek, 'and he was expelled from Oxford in 1382, mainly as a result of his teaching on the Eucharist. He went back to his rectory at Lutterworth and remained there until he died in 1384. Ironically, he . . . er . . . suffered a stroke at the very moment that the host was being elevated. But why do you think that he was not declared to be a heretic and excommunicated from the Church during his lifetime?'

'I am thankful to say that the Inquisition was not entrenched in England like it was on the Continent,' responded Melinda.

'Most of the Church leaders seem to have acted with considerable wisdom and moderation,' added Ruth.

'And after the schism broke out in 1378, the popes were too busy excommunicating each other to worry about an English academic,' said Jason with a grin.

'But, most of all, Wycliffe had powerful supporters,' insisted Wade. 'His patron for some time was John of Gaunt, third son of King Edward III, and the most powerful person in England during his father's dotage and the beginning of the reign of his young nephew, Richard II. John didn't particularly like Wycliffe's teaching on the Eucharist, but he was quite happy to have a well-known academic going around saying that secular lords should confiscate Church property. It strengthened his bargaining power with regard to the English church and the papacy. Religion and politics were thoroughly intermeshed.'

'However, in 1415 Wycliffe was condemned as a heretic by the Council of Constance,' said Christobel with a shudder, 'and his bones were dug up, burnt and cast into a river!'

'By then the aristocracy was prepared to join the Church in suppressing the Lollards because they were becoming too disruptive to the status quo,' declared Wade.

'It was most reprehensible,' said Melinda. 'As Robertson says on page 73 of his little book:

The Lollards were driven to hide themselves in the humblest ranks of society, cut off from learning and edifying conversation. They were forced into ignorance, and many were cut off also from the source of their understanding in the works of Wycliffe. There was little educated or high-ranking support, for the Church had successfully cut down their leadership. And so they became plain, meek and often timid folk, attracted by the word of God, aware of the unscriptural errors in current church practice, but powerless, except to prepare for the coming Reformation when England would be ready for the truth.

The Lollards' humble piety, their passive resistance, the shameful treatment which they bore with resignation, betrayed the pride of the priests, and stirred the most generous hearts and minds to doubts and vague desires. For a time, especially under Henry V, efforts were made to silence those doubts and quench the vague desires. The Middle Ages were temporarily restored. But it was a hopeless task. The morning star had shown the possibility of light and the dawn could not be held back.'

The phone rang and Maureen grabbed it. 'If this is someone else wanting pizza . . . Oh, Richard, it IS you. What . . .' Melinda glared at the ceiling and the rest of us waited breathlessly. Tears began to trickle slowly down Maureen's cheeks.

'What's wrong?' cried Christobel, aghast.

'It's a boy,' sobbed Maureen, 'a dear little boy.' She made an effort to pull herself together. 'What does the little chap weigh, Richard? . . . What's that in plain old pounds? . . . Good God! He's not a little chap. Eleven pounds, fifteen ounces! My poor Gail! . . . What? . . . Oh, yes, I'll be right there.

'I can go to the hospital at once,' she exclaimed, putting down the phone. 'Where's my bus timetable? Oh dear, I don't know whether I'm Arthur or Martha.'

'I will drive you,' said Christobel instantly, but she then remembered that her car was being serviced so Wade magnanimously offered to act as chauffeur. 'And I will go with you for moral support,' added Christobel. Maureen certainly looked as though she needed it. 'And Kirsty would like to have a peek at a new baby, wouldn't you Kirsty?' Kirsty nodded and they rushed off with the excited grandmother.

In the hurry, Maureen forgot to pick up the mobile phone. Melinda stared at it as if it was a poisonous reptile. 'For goodness sake, Jason, run after Maureen with that wretched thing before we have another call for pizza.' Jason obligingly set off. He didn't return.

Ruth took the opportunity to say that she had to leave to attend a meeting. That just left Melinda, Derek, Frank and me. Derek said that we might as well finish up. 'But we haven't even got to John Hus yet,' exploded Melinda. 'And this is such an important topic.'

'Perhaps next term, when we look at the Reformation,' murmured Derek uncomfortably. 'It will be something to look forward to.'

Personally, I am quite glad that we did not get onto Hus. He *was* condemned as a heretic and, unlike Wycliffe, burnt alive. The entry of a new little (or not so little) baby into the world was a much nicer way to end the tutorial.

WEEK·FIFTEEN

A new beginning?

Everyone arrived on time for our last tutorial except Jason. Ruth shocked us by revealing that he had been in a very serious accident. A car had collided with his motorbike and he had almost died. Fortunately, although he has a number of broken bones, doctors say his condition is now stable.

'Well,' said Melinda, when Ruth had finished, 'I hope that will teach him to take our mortality more seriously and to consider God's offer of salvation if we repent of our sins and accept Jesus as Lord.'

Ruth then said that Jason actually did have a near-death experience. 'After the accident, as he lay on the road, he looked up and saw his much-loved grandfather, who died several years ago. His grandfather reached out his hand and Jason felt himself leave his body and walk with his grandfather towards a bright light . . .'

'But Jason can't have been saved, because he's not a Christian,' pointed out Frank.

'I was only reading the other day that the near-death experiences experienced by non-Christians must be inspired by the devil,' commented Melinda. 'After all, only the devil can gain from people not fearing death . . .'

'Jason told me that he had never felt such peace before,'

murmured Ruth, 'not a state of mind usually associated with the devil.'

'Did he really die?' asked Kirsty breathlessly.

'When the ambulance officers arrived at the scene he had certainly stopped breathing,' replied Ruth, 'but they very quickly managed to revive him.'

'I will go and see him with my E-Team, and make sure that he understands what a narrow escape he has had from eternal damnation,' declared Melinda.

'Oh, I don't think that he is allowed to have visitors yet,' said Ruth hastily. 'Although the doctors are pleased with his progress, he is still in intensive care.'

'How did you get to see him, then?' demanded Melinda.

'He particularly asked to see me. He wanted to talk to someone about his experience, and thought of me.' Melinda looked rather put out. 'It's amazing what a small world we live in,' continued Ruth. 'Jason didn't know how to contact me, but his girlfriend Leanne was able to get Kirsty's telephone number from the leader of Kirsty's youth group, and Kirsty was able to give her Derek's number, and Derek was able to pass on mine.'

'I think that near-death experiences are absolutely fascinating,' proclaimed Christobel. 'They highlight the mystery and wonder of God, who loves all her creation and ultimately draws everyone to herself . . .' Melinda looked stern.

'How is the baby?' I quickly asked Maureen. 'Has he a name yet?'

Maureen snorted disgustedly. 'The poor little brat – they've called him Amos Paul!'

'A name from each of the Testaments,' said Ruth in a faint voice. 'Biblical names are certainly popular now.'

'Oh, he wasn't named after anyone in the Bible,' replied Maureen. 'The Amos is after Richard's great-uncle who has heaps of money and no wife or children to leave it to, so Richard and Gail are hoping that he will take an interest in little Amos. And the Paul is after Paul McCartney because Gail was listening to one of his records while she was in labour.'

'Er . . . perhaps we should now consider today's tutorial topic,' intervened Derek conscientiously. 'How would you describe the fourteenth and fifteenth centuries?'

'It was clearly a time of decline,' said Melinda. 'Huizinga says in his book *The Waning of the Middle Ages* that it was an "epoch of fading and decay". After the Black Death people were obsessed with death and dying, the Church was corrupt, scholarship was mediocre . . .'

'But it was the time of the Renaissance,' protested Christobel. 'All those wonderful scholars and artists! Leonardo da Vinci . . .'

'I am afraid that the Renaissance, while very significant, was mainly confined to Italy,' replied Melinda. 'Huizinga was writing about France and the Netherlands.'

'The revival in art and learning certainly varied from place to place,' conceded Wade. 'One thing this course has taught me is that simplistic divisions of history into periods can seriously distort our impressions of what life was like in the past. God didn't suddenly say "Let there be a Renaissance" in 1500 and behold, there was one. The fifteenth-century Renaissance grew out of the rise of towns and trade in the twelfth and thirteenth centuries, the revival of the study of the Latin classics, Roman law and Greek philosophy, the emergence of universities, better educated lay people . . .'

'But some big-headed Renaissance scholars thought that they were part of a wonderful "rebirth" or "renaissance" of culture,' added Maureen, 'and everything between them and the glorious days of the Roman Empire was a "middle age" or "dark age" of barbarity, ignorance and superstition. I read that that idea really appealed to early Protestant historians, too. I suppose it helped them justify the Reformation. The medieval Church was nasty and corrupt, and they were returning to the golden age of the early Church.'

'The fourteenth and fifteenth centuries did witness many changes,' put in Derek. 'Perhaps it could be described as a period of transition.'

'But history never stands still!' argued Christobel. 'The world is constantly changing. What period is not a period of transition?'

'Yet there is always considerable continuity as well,' said Wade. 'It is only in retrospect that you can see how profound the changes really were.'

'Take Amos Paul, for instance,' said Maureen. 'A new life is beginning, sure enough, but the poor kid is saddled with his parent's choice of name, his grandfather's nose and his aunty's red hair. And that reminds me, I have an announcement to make: I've decided, for the sake of Gail and Amos Paul, to give my ex another chance. However, I'm making it very clear that I will try to forgive but I cannot forget. There's no way that I'm going back to being a doormat. He can iron his own shirts in future, and he'll have to help out with the cooking and the shopping . . .' Christobel gave her a hug.

'It's true that we live with change and continuity all the time,' remarked Ruth. 'Jason, now, has certainly had a dramatic experience – his life will never be the same again – but he is still able to be cheeky to the nurses!'

'I think that we should pray for Jason and Maureen,' said Frank suddenly. I am not really comfortable praying aloud, and I don't think Kirsty and Derek are either, but everyone managed to saw a few words, Frank interrupting with lots of 'Amens' and 'Praise the Lords'.

When we finished Christobel produced some champagne and home-made cakes. She had brought them along so that we could celebrate the end of the course and Maureen's first grandchild. The cakes were delicious. Derek thanked her and said that she must have spent all the last week baking.

'Well, actually I just pulled them out of the freezer,' Christobel admitted. 'They were left over from my last social concerns group meeting.'

Wade proposed a toast to the new baby, and Ruth proposed one to Maureen and the 'renaissance' of her marriage. Christobel then raised her glass to all the wonderfully brave women who had striven against the odds to follow Christ through history, and Wade did likewise, in honour of the countless millions of 'ordinary' people who left no record of their existence for us to study. Melinda entered into the spirit of things and proposed a toast to the Christians who preserved the Bible throughout the Middle Ages and protested against abuses in the Church, and Frank remembered the Holy Spirit, ever guiding and sustaining us.

But it was Maureen, looking rather flushed, who had the last word. 'To us – for getting through another term.'

We all said Amen.

Suggested further reading

General reading

Barber, M. *The Two Cities, Medieval Europe 1050–1320*. London and New York: Routledge, 1992.

Collins, R. *Early Medieval Europe 300–1000*. Houndmills, Basingstoke: Macmillan, 1991.

Cook, W. and Herzman, R. *The Medieval Worldview: An Introduction*. New York and Oxford: Oxford University Press, 1983.

Dickenson, J. C. *The Later Middle Ages: From the Norman Conquest to the Eve of the Reformation*. London: A. & C. Black, 1979.

Erickson, C. *The Medieval Vision: Essays in History and Perception*. New York: Oxford University Press, 1976.

Grabois, A. *The Illustrated Encyclopedia of Medieval Civilization*. London: Octopus Books, 1980.

Hay, D. *The Medieval Centuries*. Revised edition. London: Methuen, 1964.

Hay, D. *Europe in the Fourteenth and Fifteenth Centuries*. London: Longmans, 1966.

Holmes, G., ed. *The Oxford Illustrated History of Medieval Europe*. Oxford: Oxford University Press, 1988.

Le Goff, J. *Medieval Civilization*. Translated by J. Barrow. Oxford: Basil Blackwell, 1988.

Le Goff, J., ed. *Medieval Callings*. Translated by L. Cochrane. Chicago and London: University of Chicago Press, 1987.

Painter, S. A *History of the Middle Ages 284–1500*. London: Macmillan, 1969.

Price, B. B. *Medieval Thought: An Introduction*. Cambridge, Massachusetts and Oxford: Blackwell Publishers, 1992.

Southern, R. W. *The Making of the Middle Ages*. London: The Cresset Library, 1967.

Wallace-Hadrill, J. M. *Early Medieval History*. Oxford: Basil Blackwell, 1975.

Wilkinson, B. *The Later Middle Ages in England 1216–1485*. London: Longmans, 1969.

The medieval church

Baldwin, M. W. *The Medieval Church*. The Development of Western Civilization. Ithaca, New York: Cornell University Press, 1953.

Barraclough, G. *The Medieval Papacy*. London: Thames & Hudson, 1968.

Bredero, A. *Christendom and Christianity in the Middle Ages: The Relations Between Religion, Church and Society*. Translated by R. Bruinsma. Grand Rapids, Michigan: William B. Eerdmans Publishing Company, 1994.

Brooke, R. and Brooke, C. *Popular Religion in the Middle Ages: Western Europe 1000–1300*. London: Thames & Hudson, 1984.

Comby, J. *How to Reach Church History, Vol. 1: From the Beginnings to the Fifteenth Century*. Translated by J. Bowden and M. Lydamore. London: SCM Press, 1985.

Cross, L. and Livingstone, E., eds. *The Oxford Dictionary of the Christian Church*. Second edition. Oxford: Oxford University Press, 1974.

Deanesly, M. A *History of the Medieval Church, 590–1500*. Ninth edition. London: Methuen, 1969.

Dowley, T., et al. *The History of Christianity*. Berkhamsted, Herts.: Lion Publishing, 1977.

Edwards, D. *Christian England, Vol. 1: Its Story to the Reformation*. Revised edition. London: Fount Paperbacks, 1982.

Finucane, R. C. *Miracles and Pilgrims: Popular Beliefs in Medieval*

England, London: J. M. Dent, 1979.

Geary, P. J. *Furta Sacra: Thefts of Relics in the Central Middle Ages.* Revised edition. Princeton, New Jersey: Princeton University Press, 1990.

Gonzalez, J. *A History of Christian Thought, Vol. 2: From Augustine to the Reformation.* Nashville and New York: Abingdon Press, 1971.

Hamilton, B. *Religion in the Medieval West.* London: Edward Arnold, 1986.

Kelly, J. N. D. *The Oxford Dictionary of Popes.* Oxford and New York: Oxford University Press, 1986.

Knowles, D. and Obolensky, D. *The Christian Centuries, Vol. 2: The Middle Ages.* London: Darton, Longman & Todd, 1969.

Leclercq, J., et al. *A History of Christian Spirituality, Vol. 2: The Spirituality of the Middle Ages.* London: Burns and Oates, 1968.

Morris, C. *The Papal Monarchy: The Western Church from 1050 to 1250.* Oxford History of the Christian Church. Oxford: Clarendon Press, 1989.

Southern, R. W. *Western Society and the Church in the Middle Ages.* The Pelican History of the Church. Harmondsworth: Penguin, 1970.

Tellenbach, G. *The Church in Western Europe from the Tenth to the Early Twelfth Century.* Translated by T. Reuther. Cambridge: Cambridge University Press, 1993.

Ullmann, W. *A Short History of the Papacy in the Middle Ages.* London: Methuen, 1972.

Ward, B. *Miracles and the Medieval Mind.* Revised edition. Aldershot, Hants.: Wildwood House Ltd., 1987.

Woodbridge, J. D., ed. *Great Leaders of the Christian Church.* Chicago: Moody Press, 1988.

Collections of primary sources

Barry, C. J., ed. *Readings in Church History, Vol. 1: From Pentecost to the Protestant Revolt.* Paramus, New Jersey and New York: Newman Press, 1960.

Petry, R. C., ed. *A History of Christianity: Readings in the History of the Church*, Vol. 1: *The Early and Medieval Church*. Grand Rapids, Michigan: Baker Book House, 1962.

And in particular . . .

WEEK TWO *The Franks*

Brown, P. 'Relics and Social Status in the Age of Gregory of Tours' in P. Brown, *Society and the Holy in Late Antiquity*. London: Faber and Faber, 1982.

Gregory of Tours. *The History of the Franks*. Translated by L. Thorpe. London: Penguin Classics, 1974.

James, E. *The Origins of France: From Clovis to the Capetians*. New Studies in Medieval History. Basingstoke and London: Macmillan, 1982.

James, E. *The Franks*. The Peoples of Europe. Oxford: Basil Blackwell, 1988.

Wallace-Hadrill, J. M. *The Barbarian West 400–1000*. Revised edition. Oxford: Basil Blackwell, 1985.

Wallace-Hadrill, J. M. *The Frankish Church*. Oxford: Clarendon Press, 1983.

WEEK THREE *The Anglo-Saxons*

Bede. *A History of the English Church and People*. Translated by L. Sherley-Price. Revised by R. Latham. Harmondsworth: Penguin Classics, 1968.

Blair, P. H. *The World of Bede*. Cambridge: Cambridge University Press, 1990.

Mackey, J. P., ed. *An Introduction to Celtic Christianity*. Edinburgh: T. & T. Clark, 1989.

Mayr-Harding, H. *The Coming of Christianity to Anglo-Saxon England*. London: Batsford, 1972.

Richards, J. *Consul of God: The Life and Times of Gregory the Great*. London: Routledge & Kegan Paul, 1980.

Ward, B. *The Venerable Bede*. Outstanding Christian Thinkers Series. London: Geoffrey Chapman, 1990.

WEEK FOUR *The Carolingians*

Barraclough, G. *The Crucible of Europe: The Ninth and Tenth Centuries in European History*. London: Thames & Hudson, 1976.

Ganshof, F. L. *The Carolingians and the Frankish Monarchy*. Studies in Carolingian History. Translated by J. Sondheimer. London: Longmans, 1971.

Halphen, L. *Charlemagne and the Carolingian Empire*. Translated by G. de Nie. Europe in the Middle Ages Selected Studies. Amsterdam: North Holland Publishing Company, 1977.

Herrin, J. *The Formation of Christendom*. Revised edition. Princeton, New Jersey: Princeton University Press, 1989.

McKitterick, R. *The Frankish Kingdom Under the Carolingians 751–987*. London and New York: Longmans, 1983.

Ullmann, W. *A Short History of the Papacy in the Middle Ages*. London: Methuen, 1972.

Wallace-Hadrill, J. M. *The Barbarian West 400–1000*. Revised edition. Oxford: Basil Blackwell, 1985.

WEEK FIVE *Monasticism*

Boucher, C. B. *Sword, Miter and Cloister: Nobility and the Church in Burgundy, 980–1198*. Ithaca, New York and London: Cornell University Press, 1987.

Farmer, D. H., ed. *Benedict's Disciples*. Leominster, Hereford.: Fowler Wright Books, 1980.

Fry, T., ed. *MS 1980. The Rule of St Benedict: In Latin and English with Notes*. Collegeville, Minnesotta: The Liturgical Press, 1980.

Hartcher, G. 'Witness to an Alternative: Cluny and its World in the Year 1000' in *Tjurunga*, Australasian Benedictine Review, May 1990, pp. 13–21.

Knowles, D. *Christian Monasticism*. World University Library. London: Weidenfeld & Nicolson, 1969.

Lawrence, C. H. *Medieval Monasticism: Forms of Religious Life in Western Europe in the Middle Ages*. London: Longmans, 1984.

Southern, R. W. *Western Society and the Church in the Middle Ages*.

Pelican History of the Church. Harmondsworth: Penguin, 1970.

Turpin, J. *Women in Church History: Twenty Stories for Twenty Centuries*. Cincinnati, Ohio: St Anthony Messenger Press, 1990. (Seventh Century: Hilda of Whitby; Eighth Century: Lioba, Anglo-Saxon missionary to Germany)

Wilson, K. M., ed. *Medieval Women Writers*. Athens, Georgia: University of Georgia Press, 1984. (Hrotsvit)

WEEK SIX *The papacy*

Barraclough, G. *The Medieval Papacy*. London: Thames & Hudson, 1968.

Morris, C. *The Papal Monarchy: The Western Church from 1050 to 1250*. Oxford History of the Christian Church. Oxford: Clarendon Press, 1989.

Tellenbach, G. *The Church in Western Europe from the Tenth to the Early Twelfth Century*. Translated by T. Reuther. Cambridge: Cambridge University Press, 1993.

Tierney, B. *The Crisis of Church and State 1050–1300*. Englewood Cliffs, New Jersey: Prentice-Hall, 1964.

Turpin, J. *Women in Church History: Twenty Stories for Twenty Centuries*. Cincinnati, Ohio: St Anthony Messenger Press, 1990. (Tenth Century: Adelaide, Empress of the Holy Roman Empire)

Ullmann, W. *The Growth of Papal Government in the Middle Ages*. Revised edition. London: Methuen & Co., 1965.

Ullmann, W. *A Short History of the Papacy in the Middle Ages*. London: Methuen, 1972.

WEEK SEVEN *The crusades*

Cohn, N. *The Pursuit of the Millennium: Revolutionary Millenarians and Mystical Anarchists of the Middle Ages*. Revised edition. New York: Oxford University Press, 1970.

Finucane, R. C. *Soldiers of the Faith: Crusaders and Moslems at War*. London and Melbourne: J. M. Dent & Sons, 1983.

Mayer, H. E. *The Crusades*. Translated by J. Gillingham. London: Oxford University Press, 1972.

Murphy, T. P., ed. *The Holy War*. Columbus, Ohio: Ohio State University Press, 1976.

Riley-Smith, J. *The First Crusade and the Idea of Crusading*. London: Athlone Press, 1986.

Riley-Smith, J. *The Crusades: A Short History*. New Haven and London: Yale University Press, 1987.

Runciman, S. *The History of the Crusades*. Three volumes. Cambridge: Cambridge University Press, 1951–1954.

Runciman, S. *The First Crusade*. Abridged edition of Vol. 1 of *The History of the Crusades*. Cambridge: Cambridge University Press, 1980.

WEEK EIGHT *The twelfth-century Renaissance*

Brooke, C. *The Twelfth-Century Renaissance*. London: Thames & Hudson, 1969.

Cook, W. and Herzman, R. *The Medieval Worldview: An Introduction*. New York and Oxford: Oxford University Press, 1983.

Ferruolo, S. C. 'The Twelfth-Century Renaissance', in W. Threadgold, ed. *Renaissances Before the Renaissance: Cultural Revivals of Late Antiquity and the Middle Ages*. Standford, California: Stanford University Press, 1984.

Morris, C. *The Papal Monarchy: The Western Church from 1050 to 1250*. Oxford History of the Christian Church. Oxford: Clarendon Press, 1989.

Southern, R. W. *The Making of the Middle Ages*. London: The Cresset Library, 1967.

Ward, B. *Signs and Wonders: Saints, Miracles and Prayer from the Fourth Century to the Fourteenth*. Variorum, 1992.

WEEK NINE *New religious orders*

Brunn, E. Z. and Epiney-Burgard, G. *Women Mystics in Medieval Europe*. New York: Paragon House, 1989.

The Cistercian World: Monastic Writings of the Twelfth Century. Translated and edited by P. Matarasso. London: Penguin Classics, 1993.

Elkins, S. *Holy Women of Twelfth-Century England*. Chapel Hill and London: University of North Carolina Press, 1988.

Flanagan, S. *Hildegard of Bingen, 1098–1179: A Visionary Life*. London: Routledge, 1990.

Forey, A. *The Military Orders From the Twelfth to the Early Fourteenth Centuries*. Toronto and Buffalo: University of Toronto Press, 1992.

Gervers, M., ed. *The Second Crusade and the Cistercians*. New York: St Martin's Press, 1992.

Lawrence, C. H. *Medieval Monasticism: Forms of Religious Life in Western Europe in the Middle Ages*. London: Longmans, 1984.

Leyser, H. *Hermits and the New Monasticism: A Study of Religious Communities in Western Europe, 1000–1150*. London: Macmillan Press, 1984.

Morris, C. *The Papal Monarchy: The Western Church from 1050 to 1250*. Oxford History of the Christian Church. Oxford: Clarendon Press, 1989.

Southern, R. W. *Western Society and the Church in the Middle Ages*. The Pelican History of the Church, Harmondsworth: Penguin, 1970.

WEEK TEN *Heresy*

Burman, E. *The Inquisition*. Wellingborough, Northants.: The Aquarian Press, 1984.

Erbstossler, M. *Heretics in the Middle Ages*. Translated by J. Fraser, Leipzig Edition, 1984.

Hamilton, B. *The Medieval Inquisition*. Foundations of Medieval History. London: Edward Arnold, 1981.

Lambert, M. D. *Medieval Heresy: Popular Movements from the Gregorian Reform to the Reformation*. Second edition. Oxford: Blackwells, 1992.

Moore, R. I. *The Birth of Popular Heresy*. Documents of Medieval History, 1. London: Edward Arnold, 1975.

Peters, E., ed. *Heresy and Authority in Medieval Europe: Documents in Translation*. Philadelphia: University of Pennsylvania Press, 1980.

Peters, E. *Inquisition*. Berkley, Los Angeles: University of California Press, 1989.

Shannon, A. *The Medieval Inquisition*. Second edition. Collegeville, Minnesota: Michael Glazier/The Liturgical Press, 1984.

Strayer, J. R. *The Albigensian Crusade*. Revised edition. Ann Arbor, Michigan: University of Michigan Press, 1992.

WEEK ELEVEN *St Francis of Assisi*

Boff, L. *St Francis: A Model for Human Liberation*. Translated by J. Diercksmeier. New York: Crossroad, 1982.

Bolton, B. *The Medieval Reformation*. Foundations of Medieval History. London: Edward Arnold, 1983.

Brooke, R. *The Coming of the Friars*. Historical Problems: Studies and Documents 24. London: George Allen & Unwin; New York: Barnes & Noble Books, 1975.

Francis and Clare: The Complete Works. Translated by R. Armstrong and I. Brady. Classics of Western Spirituality. New York: Paulist Press, 1982.

Moorman, J. *A History of the Franciscan Order*. Oxford: Clarendon Press, 1968.

WEEK TWELVE *Medieval women*

Baker, D., ed. *Medieval Women*. Studies in Church History Subsidia. Oxford: Basil Blackwell, 1978. (Clare)

Bancroft, A. *The Luminous Vision: Six Medieval Mystics and their Teachings*. London: George Allen & Unwin, 1982.

Jantzen, G. *Julian of Norwich*, London: SPCK, 1987.

Julian of Norwich. *Showings*. Classics of Western Spirituality. Translated by E. Colledge and J. Walsh. New York: Paulist Press, 1978.

Knowles, D. *The English Mystical Tradition*. London: Burns & Oates, 1961. (Julian and Marjorie Kempe)

Nichols, J. and Shank, L., eds. *Peaceweavers, Vol. 2: Medieval Religious Women*. Kalamazoo, Michigan: Cistercian Publications, 1987. (Clare, Christina, Julian, Anchoresses)

Turpin, J. *Women in Church History: Twenty Stories for Twenty*

Centuries. Cincinnati, Ohio: St Anthony Messenger Press, 1990. (Thirteenth Century: Clare of Assisi)

Upjohn, S. *In Search of Julian of Norwich.* London: Darton, Longman, & Todd, 1989.

Wilson, K. M., ed. *Medieval Women Writers.* Athens, Georgia: University of Georgia Press, 1984. (Julian)

WEEK THIRTEEN *The late-medieval papacy*

Barraclough, G. *The Medieval Papacy.* London: Thames & Hudson, 1968.

Crowder, C. M. D. *Unity, Heresy and Reform, 1378–1460: The Conciliar Response to the Great Schism.* Documents of Medieval History, 3. London: Edward Arnold, 1977.

Kelly, J. N. D. *The Oxford Dictionary of Popes.* Oxford and New York: Oxford University Press, 1986.

Lucki, E. *History of the Renaissance, Book 2: The Church and Religion.* Salt Lake City: University of Utah Press, 1964.

Ozment, S. *Age of Reform: An Intellectual and Religious History of Late Medieval and Reformation Europe.* New Haven and London: Yale University Press, 1980.

Tierney, B. *The Crisis of Church and State 1050–1300.* With selected documents. Englewood Cliffs, New Jersey: Prentice-Hall, 1964.

Turpin J. *Women in Church History: Twenty Stories for Twenty Centuries.* Cincinnati, Ohio: St Anthony Messenger Press, 1990. (Fourteenth Century: Catherine of Siena)

Ullmann, W. *A Short History of the Papacy in the Middle Ages.* London: Methuen, 1972.

WEEK FOURTEEN *John Wycliffe*

Hudson, A. *The Premature Reformation: Wycliffe Texts and Lollard History.* Oxford: Clarendon Press, 1988.

Kenny, A. *Wyclif* Pastmasters Series. Oxford: Oxford University Press, 1985.

Kenny, A., ed. *Wyclif In His Time.* Oxford: Clarendon Press, 1986.

McFarlane, K. *Wycliffe and the Beginnings of English Non-*

Conformity. London: English Universities Press, 1952.

Robertson, E. *John Wycliffe: Morning Star of the Reformation*. Basingstoke, Hants.: Marshall Pickering, 1984.

WEEK FIFTEEN A *new beginning?*

Aston, M. *The Fifteenth Century: The Prospect of Europe*. London: Thames & Hudson, 1968.

Huizinga, J. *The Waning of the Middle Ages: A Study of the Forms of Life, Thought and Art in France and the Netherlands in the Fourteenth and Fifteenth Centuries*. Translated by J. Hopman. Harmondsworth: Penguin, 1972.

Acknowledgements

The author would like to thank the following for permission to quote copyright material:

Cambridge University Press, Cambridge, for the quotation from *The History of the Crusades* by S. Runciman, Vol. 3, 1954, p. 480.

Macmillan Press Ltd., Basingstoke, for the quotation from *A History of the Middle Ages, 284–1500* by Sidney Painter, 1953, p. 129.

Orion Publishing Group for the quotations from *Soldiers of the Faith, Crusaders and Moslems at War* by Ronald Finucane, published by J. M. Dent, 1983, pp. 92, 98, 99, 100, 180.

Oxford University Press, Oxford, for the quotation from *History of the Franciscan Order* by John Moorman, 1968, p. 154, and the decree 'Sacrosancta' from *Documents of the Christian Church* by Henry Bettenson, 1963, p. 135.

Thames and Hudson, London, for the quotation from *Popular Religion in the Middle Ages, Western Europe 1000–1300* by Rosalind and Christopher Brookes, 1984, p. 155.

University of Pennsylvania Press, Philadelphia, for the quotation from *The First Crusade. The Chronicle of Fulcher of Chartres and Other Source Material* by Edward Peter, pp. 2–3.

Every effort has been made to trace copyright owners, and the authors and publishers apologize to anyone whose rights have inadvertently not been acknowledged. This will be corrected in any reprint.